Excel
Basic Skills

English and Mathematics

Year 2
Ages 7-8

Get the Results You Want!

Tanya Dalgleish

PASCAL
PRESS

Contents

Introduction

The **Excel** Basic Skills Workbook series aims to build and reinforce basic skills in reading, comprehension and mathematics.

The series has eight English and Mathematics core books, one for each of the school years Kindergarten/Foundation to Year 7. These are supported by teaching books, which can be used if a student needs help in a particular area of study.

The structure of this book

This book has 30 carefully sequenced double-page units. Each unit has work on Number, Measurement and Geometry in Maths, and Reading and Comprehension, Spelling and Vocabulary, and Grammar and Punctuation in English.

A student's competence in each of the 30 units can be recorded on the marking grids on pages 5 and 7. There are four end-of-term reviews. These are referred to as Tests 1 to 4. They assess a student's understanding of work covered during each term.

How to use this book

It is recommended that students complete each unit in the sequence provided because the knowledge and understanding developed in each unit is consolidated and practised in subsequent units. This workbook can be used to cover core classroom work but can also be used to provide homework and consolidation activities.

All units are written so that particular questions deal with the same areas of learning in each unit. For example, in Mathematics question 1 is always on Number (addition) and question 8 is always on Measurement (time), and so on. Similarly in the English units question 1 is always on Reading and Comprehension, and question 12 is always on Grammar and Punctuation. Question formatting is repeated throughout the workbook to support familiarity so that students can more readily deal with the Mathematics and English content.

The marking grids (see the examples on pages 4 and 6) are easy-to-use tools for recording students' progress. If you find that certain questions are repeatedly causing difficulties and errors, then there is a specific **Excel** Basic Skills Workbook to help students fully revise that topic.

These are the teaching books of the series; they will take students through the topic step by step. The use of illustrations and diagrams, practice questions, and a straightforward and simple approach will make some of the most common problem areas of English and Mathematics easy to understand and master.

Sample Maths Marking Grid

If a student is consistently getting more than **one in five** questions wrong in any area, refer to the highlighted *Excel* Basic Skills title. When marking answers on the grid, simply mark incorrect answers with 'X' in the appropriate box. This will result in a graphical representation of areas needing further work. An example has been done below for the first seven units. If a question has several parts, it should be counted as wrong if one or more mistakes are made.

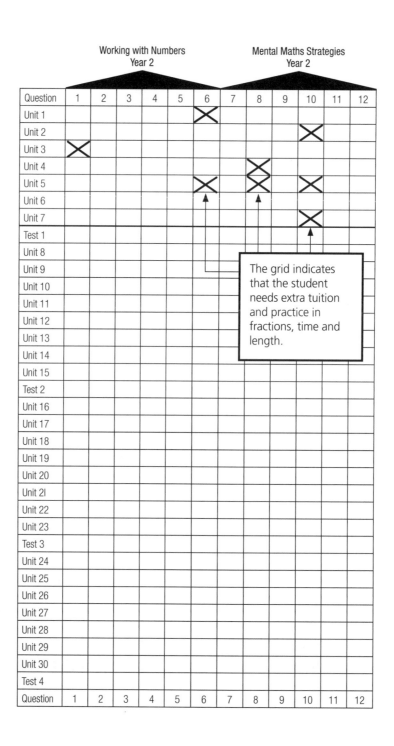

Maths Marking Grid

Question	Addition	Subtraction	Division and Multiplication	Number Language	Counting Skills	Fractions	Money	Time	Mass and Area	Length	Volume and Capacity	2D Space	3D Space	Position
	1	2	3	4	5	6	7	8	9	10	11	12	13	14
Unit 1														
Unit 2														
Unit 3														
Unit 4														
Unit 5														
Unit 6														
Unit 7														
Test 1														
Unit 8														
Unit 9														
Unit 10														
Unit 11														
Unit 12														
Unit 13														
Unit 14														
Unit 15														
Test 2														
Unit 16														
Unit 17														
Unit 18														
Unit 19														
Unit 20														
Unit 2I														
Unit 22														
Unit 23														
Test 3														
Unit 24														
Unit 25														
Unit 26														
Unit 27														
Unit 28														
Unit 29														
Unit 30														
Test 4														
Question	1	2	3	4	5	6	7	8	9	10	11	12	13	14

Sample English Marking Grid

If a student is consistently getting more than **one in five** questions wrong in any area, refer to the highlighted *Excel* Basic Skills title. When marking answers on the grid, simply mark incorrect answers with 'X' in the appropriate box. This will result in a graphical representation of areas needing further work. An example has been done below for the first seven units.

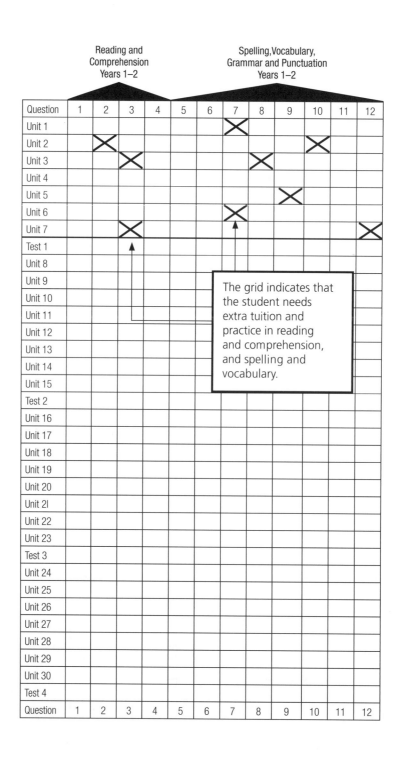

English Marking Grid

Question	Reading and Comprehension				Spelling and Vocabulary					Grammar and Punctuation		
	1	2	3	4	5	6	7	8	9	10	11	12
Unit 1												
Unit 2												
Unit 3												
Unit 4												
Unit 5												
Unit 6												
Unit 7												
Test 1												
Unit 8												
Unit 9												
Unit 10												
Unit 11												
Unit 12												
Unit 13												
Unit 14												
Unit 15												
Test 2												
Unit 16												
Unit 17												
Unit 18												
Unit 19												
Unit 20												
Unit 2I												
Unit 22												
Unit 23												
Test 3												
Unit 24												
Unit 25												
Unit 26												
Unit 27												
Unit 28												
Unit 29												
Unit 30												
Test 4												
Question	1	2	3	4	5	6	7	8	9	10	11	12

1

NUMBER

 +

5 + 4 = 9

2

10 – 4 = 6

3

Circle groups of 2.

4

∇ ∇ ∇ ∇ ∇ ∇ ∇ ∇ ∇ ∇ ∇ ∇

ten and two ones.

5

Give the hen 15 chicks.

6

Circle the pictures that show half.

7

Label the coins.

20 cents   10 cents

8

MEASUREMENT

Write today's date.

4/14/2022

9

Circle the lighter animal.

10

Use a book. Measure the length of your desk.

My desk is _____ book lengths long.

11

Tick which could hold the most marbles.

Bucket ✓   Cup _____

12

GEOMETRY

Colour the rectangles green and the circles yellow.

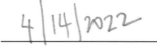

13

Circle the shape of a cereal box.

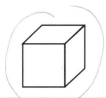

14

Draw a fish under the bridge.

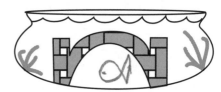

Little, Brown Bat

The little, brown bat was sleepy.
"Where will I sleep?" he said.
He looked beside the tree.
"Where will I sleep?" he said.

The little, brown bat was very
sleepy.
He looked behind the rock.
"Where will I sleep?" he said.

The little, brown bat was very,
very sleepy.
He looked inside the cave.
"I will sleep here," he said.
And he did.

READING & COMPREHENSION

1 The bat was (tired / sad / hungry).

2 The little bat was
(brown / black / red).

3 The little bat went to sleep in a

_____ .

4 The bat was looking for

_____ .

SPELLING & VOCABULARY

5 Write three words that start with *sl*.

_____   _____   _____

6 Change one letter to make a new word.

bat ___ at   pat   p ___ n   pan   p ___ n

7 Write three words that rhyme with *sleep*.

_____   _____   _____

8 Write these words in alphabetical order.

rock, bat, cave _____

9 Write the plurals.

bat _____   tree _____   cave _____

GRAMMAR & PUNCTUATION

10 Choose a noun from the box that matches the list.

stone, gravel, boulder, _____

rock, tree,
bat

11 Complete the sentence with a verb.

The bat _____ inside the cave.

12 Write the sentence correctly.   the little brown bat went to sleep in a cave

_____

1

 +

$\boxed{4}$ + $\boxed{6}$ = $\boxed{10}$

2

$\boxed{10}$ – $\boxed{6}$ = $\boxed{4}$

NUMBER

3

Circle groups of 2.

4

Write the numerals.

sixteen __16__   seventeen __17__

eighteen __18__

5

Draw 12 butterflies.

6

Colour half of each shape.

7

Label the coins.

_____   _____

8

MEASUREMENT

What is your birth date?

07002015

9

Draw a shape that covers 4 squares.

10

Use a pencil to measure the length of your desk.

My desk is _____ pencils long.

11

Estimate:
How many pencils will fill a lunchbox?

5 _____   90 _____

12

GEOMETRY

Join the dots to make a shape.
Name the shape.

• 1

4 •   • 2

_____   3 •

13

Link the objects which have a similar shape.

14

Draw a circle in the box on the right.

The Farmer and the Pig

The little pig saw the open gate and ran as fast as its little legs could carry it, away from the farmer, away from its mother and across the paddock. The farmer chased the little pig, across the paddock, through the trees, around the rocks, over the bridge and into a corn field.

The little pig stopped to eat some corn and the farmer stopped to take a rest.

The little pig stopped eating to take a rest. The farmer scooped up the tired little pig and carried it back to the farm.

READING & COMPREHENSION

1 The little pig ran (quickly / slowly / sadly).

2 The little pig grew tired and had to have a (corncob / rest / race).

3 The pig stopped running when it got to the _____ .

4 The farmer caught the pig because it was _____ .

SPELLING & VOCABULARY

5 List three words in the story that have *st* in them.

_____ _____ _____

6 Change one letter to make a new word.

pig ___ ig   dog ___ og   hog ho ___

7 The opposite of *little* is _____ .

8 Write these words in alphabetical order.

pig, gate, little _____

9 Write the plurals.

pig _____ farm _____ farmer _____

GRAMMAR & PUNCTUATION

10 Choose a noun from the story to complete the sentence.

The little pig stopped to eat some _____ .

11 Choose a verb from the story to complete the sentence.

The little pig _____ as fast as it could.

12 Write the question correctly.   why did the little pig run away

_____

1 NUMBER

$15 + 5 = \boxed{}$

2

$\boxed{20} - \boxed{} = \boxed{}$

3 Circle groups of 5.

4 Write the numerals.

fifteen _____   fourteen _____

thirteen _____

5 Circle 16 fish.

6 Draw a box around half of the birds.

7 Colour the coins which are silver.

MEASUREMENT **8**

Colour the summer months red.

December	March	June	September
January	April	July	October
February	May	August	November

9 Tick the heavier animal.

10 Circle the longer object.

11 A teacup.
Which do you think it could hold?

16 marbles _____   60 marbles _____

GEOMETRY **12** Name the shapes.

_____

_____

_____

13 Draw some things which are this shape.

14 Draw a star in the centre box.

In a Dark, Dark Wood
In a dark, dark wood there was a dark, dark garden.
In the dark, dark garden there was a dark, dark shed.
In the dark, dark shed there was a dark, dark cupboard.
In the dark, dark cupboard there was a dark, dark shelf.
On the dark, dark shelf there was a dark, dark pot.
Behind the dark, dark pot there was a dark, dark box.
Under the dark, dark box there was a SPIDER!

1 The story is set in the (dark / park / shark).

2 The spider was (attacking / hiding / scary).

3 The spider was under a

_____ .

4 What do you think the spider did when the box was lifted?

_____

5 List three words that start with *sh* like *shed*.

_____ _____ _____

6 Add one letter to make a new word.

___ p o t   ___ l a p   ___ l i p

7 Write three words which rhyme with *pot*.

_____ _____ _____

8 Write these words in alphabetical order.

box, shed, pot _____

9 Write the plurals.

box _____   shelf _____   spider _____

10 Circle the odd one out.

spider   dog   eat   tree

11 Tick the <u>verbs</u> that a spider can do.

run   black   hide   scary   crawl   body   eat   wait   legs   eyes

12 Write the sentence correctly.   look out, there's a spider

_____

1   NUMBER

 +   = ☐

12 + 0 = ☐

2   20 triangles. Cross out 10.

How many left? ☐

3   Draw 2 groups of 3 fish.

4

ten and ☐

5   Circle 14 pencils.

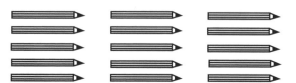

6   Divide each shape in half.

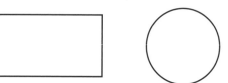

7   Colour the coins which are gold.

8   MEASUREMENT

Colour the weekend days.

Saturday   Tuesday   Sunday   Friday   Monday   Wednesday   Thursday

9   Draw a shape that covers 6 squares.

10   Draw a longer snake.

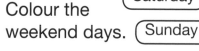

11   A teacup could hold:

10 coins _____   100 coins _____

12   GEOMETRY

Use circles to draw a cat.

13   Draw something in your room that has the same shape.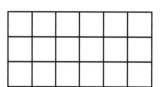

14   Draw a bowl on the table.

Spiders

Spiders are not insects. They are **arachnids**. Spiders have eight legs and each leg has seven segments.

All spiders spin silk. They use silk to make their webs, wrap up their prey and protect their eggs.

When a spider catches its prey it squirts liquid onto it to make it dissolve and then sucks it up like a drink.

READING & COMPREHENSION

1   Spiders are (insects / arachnids / webs).

2   Spiders spin (prey / silk / eggs).

3   A spider leg has _____ segments.

4   How do spiders eat?

_____

_____

SPELLING & VOCABULARY

5   Circle the words ending in *lk*.

walk   wall   silk   tall   talk   milk   drink

6   Add the word parts and write the new word.

dr + ink = _____   th + ink = _____   shr + ink = _____

7   Write three words which rhyme with *all*.

_____   _____   _____

8   Write these nouns in alphabetical order.

leg, egg, silk _____

9   Write the plurals.

leg _____   egg _____   spider _____

GRAMMAR & PUNCTUATION

10   Link the noun labels to the spider.

eyes   legs   silk

11   Complete the sentence with a verb.

Spiders _____ their victims.

12   Write the sentence correctly.   spiders are not insects

_____

Mathematics

NUMBER

1

+ 0

 + ☐ = ☐

2 20 forks. Cross out 17.

How many are left? ☐

3

☐ rows of ☐ bees.

4

Circle groups of ten. ☐ tens.

5

1st

4th

Draw who came 4th.

6 Colour half the balloons.

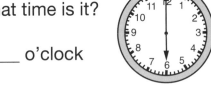

7 Colour the coin worth the most.

MEASUREMENT

8 What time is it?

_____ o'clock

9 Circle the heavier animal.

10 Draw something shorter than the pencil.

11 Colour the model that uses the most blocks.

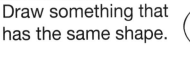

GEOMETRY

12 Use these shapes to draw a car.

13 Draw something that has the same shape.

14 Draw a hat on the person in the middle.

16

Please Come to My Party

Soo Yin's 7th Birthday

Who: Mustafa

Where: 12 Gumleaf Drive
            Riverglen

Date: 12th March

Time: 2 pm – 4 pm

RSVP: Rob and Mary
           9557 7200 by
           10th March please.

READING & COMPREHENSION

1 The party is at
(2 pm / 4 pm / lunchtime).

2 Mustafa is Soo Yin's
(father / friend / pet).

3 Soo Yin is turning _____
years old.

4 What date is the party?

_____

SPELLING & VOCABULARY

5 Write three words that start with *pl*.

_____   _____   _____

6 Choose words from the box to complete the compound words.

| light, lace |
| photo |

day _____   shoe _____   _____ graph

7 Circle the words that show how Soo Yin will feel on her birthday.

excited   angry   lonely   sad   happy   surprised   pleased

8 Write these words in alphabetical order.

party, cake, present _____

9 Write the plurals.

party _____   story _____   lady _____

10 A pronoun is a word that can replace a noun.
Choose a pronoun from the box.

| She, Her, Him |

It's Soo Yin's birthday. _____ will be 7.

GRAMMAR & PUNCTUATION

11 Complete the sentence with verbs.

At Soo Yin's party the children will _____ games and _____ food.

12 Write the question correctly.   how old will soo yin be

_____

Mathematics

1 · NUMBER

$5 + \boxed{} = 20$

$6 + \boxed{} = 20$

2

20 flowers. Cross off 4.

How many are left? $\boxed{}$

3

Circle groups of 4.

4

Circle groups of 10. $\boxed{}$ tens

5

Colour who came third.

1st

6

Colour one half of the strawberries.

7

Colour the coin worth more money.

8 · MEASUREMENT

What time is it?

_____ o'clock

9

Who has the larger shoe print?

_____

10

Circle the cat with the longest tail.

11

Draw a container that will hold more water than the jug.

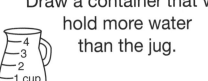

12 · GEOMETRY

Circle the shapes with 4 straight sides.

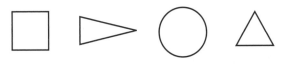

13

Circle the objects which will roll.

14

Help the rabbit find its hole.

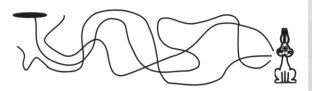

My Hands

My hands are useful.
They can
throw a ball,
peel an orange
and turn a page.
They can lift,
carry,
pull,
push,
hit,
flick,
and scratch where I itch.

1 Hands can (eat / peel / walk) an orange.

2 Hands can (kick / throw / dig) a ball.

3 Hands are very

_____ .

4 What can you do with your hands?

_____

5 Write three words that end in *nd* like *hand*.

_____ _____ _____

6 Change one letter to make a new word.

hit ___ i t   hit h ___ t   dig ___ i g   dig d ___ g

7 Write three rhyming words for *flick*.

_____ _____ _____

8 Write these words in alphabetical order.

paint, hit, dig _____

9 Write the plurals.

hand _____   ball _____   orange _____

10 Choose a pronoun to complete the sentence.

(My / Me / Us) _____ hands are useful.

11 Underline the verbs for actions you can do with your hands.

paint, draw, pitch, hands, my, me, dig, clap, type, scratch, feet, useful

12 Write the question correctly.   what can your hands do

_____

1 — NUMBER

$$9 + \boxed{} = 20$$

$$10 + \boxed{} = 20$$

2

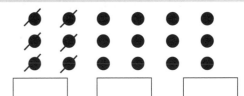

$$\boxed{} - \boxed{} = \boxed{}$$

3 Circle groups of 5.

4

2 tens = $\boxed{}$

5 Colour 17 stars.

6 Colour the shapes which show $\frac{1}{4}$.

7 Colour the coins with a value less than $1.00.

8 — MEASUREMENT

Draw 9 o'clock.

9 Draw a shape which covers 8 squares.

10 Draw a shorter person.

11 Tick the container which can be used to carry sand.

12 — GEOMETRY

Circle the shapes with 3 straight sides.

13 Circle the objects which will not roll.

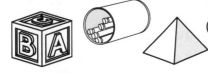

14 Draw a bee on the middle flower.

In the Sea

Here is some plankton that grew in the sea.
Here is the little fish that ate some plankton that grew in the sea.
Here is the big fish that ate the little fish that ate some plankton that grew in the sea.
Here is the shark that ate the big fish that ate the little fish that ate some plankton that grew in the sea.
Here is the shark free in the sea.

READING & COMPREHENSION

1 The little fish ate (fish / plankton / shark).

2 The shark ate (plankton / fish / sea).

3 Plankton grows in the

_____ .

4 What ate the little fish?

_____ .

SPELLING & VOCABULARY

5 Write two words from the story that have *sh* in them.

_____   _____

6 List three words that rhyme with *shark*.

_____   _____   _____

7 Write three other words that mean *big*.

_____   _____   _____

8 What smaller words can you find in *plankton*?

_____

9 Write the plurals.

fish _____   shark _____

GRAMMAR & PUNCTUATION

10 Choose a pronoun to replace *The shark* in the sentence.
<u>The shark</u> ate a fish. (She / It / I / Her / His)

11 Write five verbs for actions that a shark can do.

_____

12 Write the sentence correctly.   i like sharks

_____

NUMBER

1

$6 + 14 = \boxed{}$

$7 + \boxed{} = 20$

2

12 eggs. 3 are broken.

How many are left? $\boxed{}$

$\boxed{} - \boxed{} = \boxed{}$

3

Circle groups of 3.

Draw 3 groups of 2 fish.

4

▼ ▼ ▼ ▼ ▼ ▼ ▼ ▼ ▼ ▼ ▼ ▼

ten and $\boxed{}$

3 tens $= \boxed{}$

5

Colour 14 circles.

◯◯◯◯◯◯◯◯◯◯
◯◯◯◯◯◯◯◯◯◯

Label 1st, 2nd, 3rd and 4th.

___ ___ ___ ___

6

Divide each shape in half.

◯   ☐   △

Colour the shape that shows $\frac{1}{4}$.

7

Colour the coins with a value less than 50c.

8

MEASUREMENT

The time is _____ o'clock.

9

Draw a shape which
covers 10 squares.

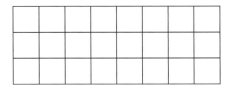

Tick the lighter animal.

10

Draw a shorter flower.

Circle the dog with the longer legs.

11

Will your lunchbox hold:

100 pegs? _____   20 pegs? _____

Order the models from
smallest to largest.

_____   _____   _____

GEOMETRY   **12**

Draw a closed
shape with 3 straight sides.

Colour the rectangles yellow
and the circles green.

13

Draw 3 things that
are this shape.

14

Draw a fish in the tank on the left.

The mouse is
(on / under / beside) the cat.

Sharks

Sharks are fish. There are more than 300 different kinds of sharks. Some sharks lay eggs and some sharks have live babies. Sharks have skeletons made of cartilage rather than bone. Sharks spend all their time looking for food. Most sharks eat fish. Some sharks eat plankton. Some sharks eat sea turtles, seals and dolphins.

Sharks will attack people if they mistake the person for an animal that is their usual food, such as a seal. A shark may also attack a human if the human is in its territory. Very few sharks are dangerous to people.

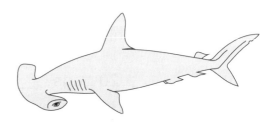

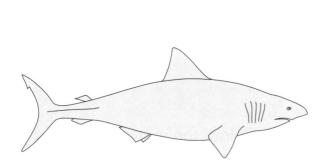

READING & COMPREHENSION

1

A shark's skeleton is made of (rubber / cartilage / bone).

2

Sharks rarely attack (fish / dolphins / people).

3

Sharks are _____ .

4

Why might a shark attack a person?

_____

_____

5

Attack ends in *ck*. Write three other words that end in *ck*.

_____ _____ _____

6 Change one letter to make new words.

eat   ___ at   pat   p ___ t   pit   pi ___

7 Write two words that rhyme with *fish*.

_____ _____

8 Can you find some smaller words in *dangerous*? Write the words.

_____

9 Write the singular of these plurals.

sharks _____   dolphins _____

turtles _____   babies _____

10 Choose a pronoun from the box to complete the sentence.

| they |
| them |
| their |

Sharks will attack people if _____ are provoked.

11 Complete the sentences with verbs.

Sharks rarely _____ people. Sharks spend all their time

_____ for food. Most sharks _____ fish.

12 Write the question correctly.
are sharks interesting creatures

_____

Mathematics

NUMBER

1

$4 + 16 = \boxed{}$

$16 + \boxed{} = 20$

2

$\boxed{} - \boxed{} = \boxed{}$

3 Circle groups of 6.

4

$\boxed{}$ tens = $\boxed{}$

5

Link: 7th   eighth

8th   seventh

9th   ninth

6 Colour the shapes which show $\frac{1}{4}$.

7 Colour the coins you would use to buy a banana costing 40c.

MEASUREMENT

8

Draw 2 o'clock.

9 Which hand print is bigger? Circle it.

10 Number the objects in order from shortest to longest.

11

Will your lunchbox hold:

6 cups of water? _____

50 cups of water? _____

GEOMETRY

12 Circle the shape that has no straight sides.

13 Circle the objects which will stack.

 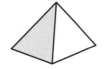

14 Draw a dog beneath the tree.

Vegetable Stir Fry

Ingredients
2 tbsp oil
1 onion, diced
1 carrot, cut into thin strips
1 cup chopped broccoli
1 cup baby corn
1 tbsp lime juice
1tbsp honey
150 mL teriyaki sauce
75 mL soy sauce
Method
Heat oil. Fry onion. Add carrot and broccoli. Cook for 1 minute. Add baby corn. Stir in sauces and heat through. Serve with steamed rice or noodles.

READING & COMPREHENSION

1 The onion is
(fried / steamed / served).

2 The sauce is
(diced / chopped / heated).

3 Honey is one

_____ in the recipe.

4 The recipe is called

_____ .

SPELLING & VOCABULARY

5 Write three words that start with *br*.

_____   _____   _____

6 Choose words from the box to make compound words.   light, room, day

bed _____   to _____   sun _____

7 Circle the noun that does not belong.

cauliflower   potato   broccoli   mango

8 Write the nouns in alphabetical order.

onion, corn, broccoli, carrot _____

9 Write the plurals.

potato _____   tomato _____

GRAMMAR & PUNCTUATION

10 Choose a noun from the box to complete the sentence.   pool, pot, pumpkin
Put the vegetables in a _____ .

11 Write five verbs for actions that you can do with vegetables.

_____

12 Use an exclamation mark and write the sentence correctly.

it's delicious _____

Mathematics

NUMBER

1

1 + 19 = ☐

19 + ☐ = 20

2

20 − 18 = ☐

20 − 2 = ☐

3

☐ rows of ☐ crosses.

4

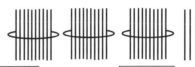

☐ tens and ☐ ones = 37

5

Draw 19 stars.

6

Divide the cake into quarters.

7

Colour the coins you would use to buy a pencil for 50c.

MEASUREMENT

8

What time is it?

_____

9

A mouse is lighter than a cat.

True _____   False _____

10

Colour the longest worm.

11

Circle the correct answer.
The jug will hold (more / less) water than the cup.

12

GEOMETRY

Trace the oval shape.

How many sides? _____

How many corners? _____

13

Circle the objects which will not stack.

14

The fish is (in / above / under) the tank.

Favourite Food

My favourite food is pizza. Homemade pizza can be healthy, especially if you have toppings such as tomato, mushrooms, capsicum and onions. I like lots of cheese on my pizza. Cheese has calcium which is good for building strong teeth and bones. I also like chicken on my pizza. It provides protein for building muscles. The pizza base is like bread. It is food for energy. Sometimes I put pineapple on my pizza and that's healthy too because it's fruit.

READING & COMPREHENSION

1 Cheese is good for (muscles / energy / bones).

2 Protein is good for (teeth / pizza / muscles).

3 Pizza base is like

_____ .

4 What fruit can go on pizza?

_____

SPELLING & VOCABULARY

5 Write three words that start with *ch*.

_____   _____   _____

6 Make little words using the letters in *pineapple*.

_____

7 Write the opposites.

strong _____   lucky _____   good _____

8 Cross out the incorrect words.

I went (to / two / too) the pizza shop.

9 Write the singular of these words.

men _____   women _____   children _____

GRAMMAR & PUNCTUATION

10 Circle the nouns used to make pizza.

tomato, cheese, eat, chicken, muscles, favourite, should, tasty, pineapple

11 Complete the sentence with a verb.

I like _____ pizza.

12 Answer with a sentence. What kind of pizza is your favourite?

_____

Mathematics

NUMBER

1

$2 + 3 + 5 =$ ☐

$1 + 4 + 5 =$ ☐

2

$20 - 6 =$ ☐

$20 - 14 =$ ☐

3 Draw 2 rows of 5 fish.

4

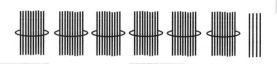

☐ tens and ☐ ones =

5 Write the even numbers to 10.

_____ , _____ , _____ , _____ , _____

6 Link:

$\dfrac{1}{4}$

$\dfrac{1}{2}$

MEASUREMENT

7 Colour the coins with a value less than 50c.

8 Draw 5 o'clock.

9 Which has the greater area —your foot or your hand?

_____

10 Draw a star on the shorter tree.

GEOMETRY

11 Name something that will hold more water than your bathtub.

_____

12 Colour the shape with no corners.

13 Circle the like shapes.

14 The worm is (in / under / on) the apple.

Friends

Friends are very important people. Friends play with you. They help you do things. They share with you. They make you laugh. They look after you when you are sad or hurt. They make you feel happy.

My best friend is Aisha. She came to Australia from Afghanistan two years ago. I helped her learn to speak English. She is teaching me to say some words in Pashto. She writes in Pashto from right to left. The Pashto alphabet looks very different. Aisha is clever.

1 READING & COMPREHENSION

Friends (share / live / play) their things.

2

Friends are (hateful / helpful / hurtful).

3

Some people in Afghanistan speak
_____ .

4

Friends look after you if you
_____ yourself.

SPELLING & VOCABULARY

5 Link pairs of words that rhyme.

thing   thick   day   play   chalk   ring   stick   talk

6 Antonyms are words with opposite meanings. Write antonyms.

unimportant _____   happy_____   teach _____

7 Add the silent letters.

fr____end   We____nesday   ____nock

8 Write the nouns in alphabetical order.

friend, children, people _____

9 Write the plurals of these words.

person _____   child _____   friend _____

10 GRAMMAR & PUNCTUATION

Circle a pronoun to complete the sentence.

(My / His / Her / I / Me) best friend's name is Aisha.

11 Write a verb to complete the sentence.

Friends _____ each other.

12 Answer with a sentence. What is your best friend's name?

_____

NUMBER

1

$$5 + 5 + 5 = \boxed{}$$

$$5 + 5 + 4 = \boxed{}$$

2

$$20 - 13 = \boxed{}$$

$$20 - 7 = \boxed{}$$

3 Draw 3 rows of 4 bees.

4 Write the numerals.

twenty-seven _____   thirty-four_____

fifty-one _____

5 Write the missing numbers.

10, ____, 14, ____, 18, 20

6 Link:

$\frac{1}{4}$

$\frac{1}{2}$

$\frac{1}{4}$

MEASUREMENT

7 Which coin has an echidna? _____

Which coin shows a platypus? _____

8 The time is half past

_____ .

9 Colour the shape with the smaller area.

10 Colour the longest fish.

11 Name something that will hold less water than your kitchen sink.

_____

GEOMETRY

12 Draw a triangle inside a circle.

13 Underline the words that describe the object. (curly / flat / smooth / pointed / round / sharp)

14 Draw a spoon in the bowl.

English

Shopping List

sesame oil	bok choy
bean sprouts	spring onions
garlic	fresh ginger
apples	pineapple
bananas	mango
fish sauce	coconut milk
powdered ginger	
dried chillies	
jasmine rice	
dried rice noodles	
fresh egg noodles	
chicken thighs	

READING & COMPREHENSION

1 The shopping list contains four kinds of (noodles / cheese / fruit).

2 We need to buy fish (eggs / sauce / fillets).

3 You can buy noodles fresh and _____ .

4 What two items would you add to the shopping list?
_____

SPELLING & VOCABULARY

5 Cross out the incorrect word.

The shopping list contains coconut (butter / shell / milk).

6 Write rhyming words from the text.

nice _____ soil _____ mean _____

7 Circle the one that does not belong.

rice   apples   oranges   bananas

8 Number the words in alphabetical order.

rice ____   mango ____   banana ____

9 Write the plurals.

noodle _____ rice _____ chilli _____

GRAMMAR & PUNCTUATION

10 Use an adjective from the box.

The shopping list says to buy _____ egg noodles.

| dried, fresh, powdered |

11 Circle the verbs that describe what you can do with vegetables.

chop, slice, shred, beans, carrots, potatoes, steam, fry, boil, broccoli

12 Write the command correctly. Use commas to separate words in a list.

buy apples oranges bananas rice and bread _____

Mathematics

1 | 2

NUMBER

1
$$15 + 5 = \boxed{}$$
$$5 + 15 = \boxed{}$$

2
$$19 = 20 - \boxed{}$$
$$20 - \boxed{} = 19$$

3 Draw 3 groups of 5 worms.

4
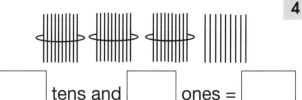

$\boxed{}$ tens and $\boxed{}$ ones = $\boxed{}$

5 Write the odd numbers up to 10.

_____ , _____ , _____ , _____ , _____

6 Colour $\frac{1}{4}$ of the shoes.

7 How much money altogether?

_____

MEASUREMENT

8 The time is half past

_____ .

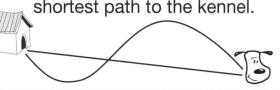

9 Draw a shape which covers 12 squares.

10 Use a red pencil to trace the shortest path to the kennel.

11 Colour the model that uses the least number of blocks.

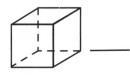

GEOMETRY

12 Draw a pattern using zig zag and straight lines.

13 How many faces does each shape have?

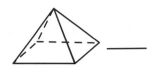 ____   ____

14 Help the lost puppy find its way home.

Water Wise

Our class, 2M, has been learning about the importance of saving water.

We learned that many people around the world don't have water in their homes. Some children spend hours every day fetching water from rivers, lakes or wells.

Students in our class tried carrying buckets of water across the playground. Water is very heavy. It was hard work.

1 Many people don't have (homes / water / buckets) in their homes.

2 Children in some countries (carry / drive / splash) water to their homes.

3 It is important not to waste

_____ .

4 How can you save water?

_____ .

5 Write three words from the text that rhyme.

mend_____   say_____   grass_____

6 Cross out the incorrect words. Children carry water to (there / their) homes. We (tired / tried) to carry the water.

7 Fill in the missing letters.

    pe_____ple   he_____vy   _____ours

8 Write the words in alphabetical order.

lakes, wells, rivers _____

9 Write the singular of these words.

countries _____   people _____   children _____

10 Choose words from the box to make compound words.

_____fall   _____room   _____ground

| play, water, class |

11 Complete the command with a verb.

_____ the leaky tap.

12 Write the sentence correctly. all people plants and animals need water

_____

NUMBER

1

$$17 + 3 = \boxed{}$$

$$3 + \boxed{} = 20$$

2

$$20 - 7 = \boxed{}$$

$$20 - 8 = \boxed{}$$

3 Draw 2 groups of 5 apples.

4 Write the numeral for
7 tens and 3 ones.

_____

5 Write the odd numbers less than 20.

_____

_____

6 Colour $\frac{1}{2}$ the circle.

7 I gave the shopkeeper 50c.

I bought

How much change will I get? _____

MEASUREMENT

8 Draw half past 12.

9 Colour the shape with the smaller area.

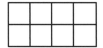

10 Circle the face with the longest hair.

11 Circle the models with the same volume.

GEOMETRY

12 This is a hexagon.

How many sides? _____

How many corners? _____

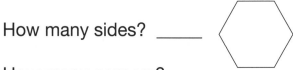

13 Colour the objects which match this shape.

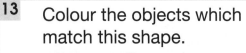

14 Colour the flower which has a bee under it.

Bee Stings

Bees are insects. They have six legs and three body parts. Bees have three single eyes on top of their heads and two large compound eyes. Bees have stingers to pump poison into victims. When a bee uses its stinger the stinger stays in the victim's skin and the bee dies. A bee sting can be deadly if the person is allergic to the bee's poison. Bees don't sting people unless they have been annoyed. It is best to leave bees alone.

1 Bees have (two / three / four) body parts.

2 Bees have (two / three / five / seven) eyes.

3 Some people are

_____ to bee stings.

4 It's best to leave bees

_____ .

5 Underline the words that start with the same *th* sound as *they*.

thistle   thought   this   the   things   thanks   then   Thursday

6 Write the words.

st + ing _____   sk + in _____   scr + ape _____

7 Add the prefix *un* to change the word meanings.

_____happy   _____do   _____important

8 Number the words in alphabetical order.

allergy ____   eyes ____   pump ____

9 Write the plurals.

bee _____   sting _____   poison _____

10 Add noun labels for the bee.

11 Complete the sentence with a verb.

Bees _____ when they sting something.

12 Use (" ") to write the sentence correctly. it is best to leave bees alone said mum _____

Mathematics

NUMBER

1

$18 + 2 =$ ▢

$2 +$ ▢ $= 20$

2

$20 - 0 =$ ▢

$20 -$ ▢ $= 0$

3

Draw 3 groups of 6 flowers.

4

Write the numeral for
4 tens and 5 ones.

_____

5

Write the missing numbers.

10, ____ , 30, ____ , 50,

____ , 70, ____ , 90, ____

6

What part of the
shape is coloured?

_____

7

How much money
altogether?

 　_____

MEASUREMENT

8

Draw quarter
past 11.

9

A toothbrush is heavier
than a chair.

True ____　　False ____

10

Draw a taller
person.

11

Colour the model with the
larger volume.

GEOMETRY

12

Draw the mirror half.

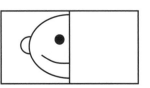

13

Colour the shapes with
curved surfaces.

14

The car is
(in front of /
beside)
the house.

The Octopus

The body of the octopus is like a bag with eight long arms. Each arm is lined with suckers. The octopus lives alone in caves or beneath rocks on the ocean floor. It crawls around on the ocean floor looking for food such as shellfish.

Its worst enemy is the moray eel. If the octopus is losing a fight with an eel the octopus can release a squirt of black ink to hide behind while it escapes. If it loses an arm in the fight the arm can grow back.

1 An octopus has (six / eight / ten) arms.

2 An octopus has (suckers / fingers / hands) all along its arms.

3 The worst enemy of the octopus is the _____ .

4 What happens if an octopus loses an arm? _____

5 Write three words that start with *cr*.

_____   _____   _____

6 Add one letter to make a new word.

eel ___ e e l   eel ___ e e l   stay st ___ a y

7 The prefix *oct* means eight. Write other words starting with *oct*.

_____

8 Write the words in alphabetical order.

octopus, eel, shark _____

9 Write the plurals.

boy _____   eel _____   enemy _____

10 Add noun labels for the octopus.

11 Complete the sentence with a verb.

An octopus will _____ with a moray eel.

12 Answer with a sentence. Where do octopuses live?

_____

Mathematics

NUMBER

1

14 + 6 = ☐

6 + 14 = ☐

2

10 = 20 − ☐

12 = 20 − ☐

3 Circle groups of 4.

4 Link:

twenty-five   25

thirty   31

thirty-one   30

5 Write the missing numbers.

a) 90, 91, ____ , 93

b) 78, 79, 80, ____

6 What part of the shape is coloured?

_____

7 Circle the piggy bank with the most money.

MEASUREMENT

8 Circle the clock that shows half past 12.

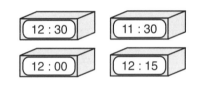

12 : 30   11 : 30

12 : 00   12 : 15

9 Colour the shape with the smallest area.

10 Draw a bee on the shortest flower.

11 Circle the container with the largest capacity.

GEOMETRY

12 Name the shapes.

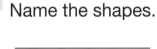 _____

 _____

_____

13 Colour the shapes which have flat faces or surfaces.

14 Draw a girl on the right of the dog.

Cats Love . . .

Cats love to prowl the yard at night
—prowl, stalk, roam, pounce.
Cats love to sleep in the sun all day
—prrrr, yawn, prrrr, sigh.
Cats love to eat their favourite foods
—munch, crunch, lap, lick.
Cats love to clean their whiskers and fur
—lick, preen, wipe, groom.
I love cats!

PRRRRRRRRRRRRRR

READING & COMPREHENSION

1 Cats love to clean their (beds / food / fur).

2 Cats love to (sleep / prowl / clean) in the sun all day.

3 Cats love to eat their favourite _____ .

4 List the sounds that cats make in the poem. _____
_____

SPELLING & VOCABULARY

5 Change *y* to *i* and add *ly* to these words.

noisy _____   happy _____

6 Write the words.

cr + unch _____   pr + een _____   cl + ean _____

7 Circle the words that mean the same as *eat*.

preen   munch   nibble   pounce   devour   groom

8 *Sun* and *son* are homophones. Write homophones for these words.

there _____   flour _____   sail _____

9 Write the plurals. Some words don't change from singular to plural.

sheep _____   deer _____   salmon _____

GRAMMAR & PUNCTUATION

10 Draw a picture of a cat and label it with nouns.

11 Circle the verbs for actions that a cat can do.

lick, tickle, chin, nose, rub, night, whiskers, fur, munch, crunch, sleep

12 Answer with a sentence. How do you feel about cats?

_____

1 NUMBER

$4 + 5 + 1 = \boxed{}$

$3 + 3 + 4 = \boxed{}$

2

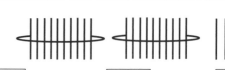

$\boxed{} - \boxed{} = \boxed{}$

$20 - 12 = \boxed{}$

$20 - 10 = \boxed{}$

3

Draw 4 groups of 2 ice-creams.

4

$\boxed{}$ tens and $\boxed{}$ ones = $\boxed{}$

Write the numeral for 4 tens and 2 ones.

_____

5

Write the missing numbers.

a) 2, ____ , 6, 8, ____ , ____ ,

____ , ____ , 18, ____ .

b) 70, ____ , 50, ____ , ____ .

6

Colour the shapes that show quarters.

7

Colour the coins you would use to buy a pen costing 60c.

8 MEASUREMENT

Draw half past 7.

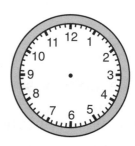

Answers

UNIT **1** page 8

Maths
1. 4, 9
2. 6
3. Parent/teacher to check.
4. 2
5. Parent/teacher to check.
6. circle, triangle
7. 20c, 10c
8. Parent/teacher to check.
9. fish
10. Parent/teacher to check.
11. bucket
12. Parent/teacher to check.
13. cube on the left
14. Parent/teacher to check.

English
1. tired
2. brown
3. cave
4. somewhere to sleep
5. e.g. sleep, slip, slide, slam, slit
6. e.g. pat, pan, pen
7. e.g. peep, sheep, keep, leap, beep
8. bat, cave, rock
9. bats, trees, caves
10. rock
11. slept / looked
12. The little brown bat went to sleep in a cave.

UNIT **2** page 10

Maths
1. 4, 6, 10
2. 4
3. Parent/teacher to check.
4. 16, 17, 18
5. Parent/teacher to check.
6. Parent/teacher to check.
7. 50c, $2
8. Parent/teacher to check.
9. Parent/teacher to check.
10. Parent/teacher to check.
11. 90
12. diamond / square

13. block and Rubik's cube; pencil and drum
14. Parent/teacher to check.

English
1. quickly
2. corncob
3. cornfield
4. tired
5. stopped, fast, rest
6. e.g. dig, hog, hop
7. big
8. gate, little, pig
9. pigs, farms, farmers
10. corn, corncobs
11. ran
12. Why did the little pig run away?

UNIT **3** page 12

Maths
1. 20
2. 11, 9
3. Parent/teacher to check.
4. 15, 14, 13
5. Parent/teacher to check.
6. Parent/teacher to check.
7. 50c, 10c, 5c, 20c
8. December, January, February
9. elephant
10. leaf
11. 16
12. circle, square, triangle
13. Parent/teacher to check.
14. Parent/teacher to check.

English
1. dark
2. hiding
3. box
4. e.g. Ran away.
5. e.g. ship, shed, shout, shelf, share, shin
6. e.g. spot, slap, slip
7. e.g. cot, dot, spot, lot, rot
8. box, pot, shed
9. boxes, shelves, spiders
10. eat (it's the only verb)
11. run, hide, crawl, eat, wait
12. Look out, there's a spider!

UNIT **4** page 14

Maths
1. 12
2. 10
3.
4. 5
5. Parent/teacher to check.
6.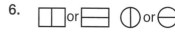
7. $2, $1 coins
8. Saturday, Sunday
9. Parent/teacher to check.
10. Parent/teacher to check.
11. 10
12. Parent/teacher to check.
13. e.g. pencil holder, mug, soft drink can
14. Parent/teacher to check.

English
1. arachnids
2. silk
3. 7
4. They dissolve food and then drink it.
5. walk, silk, talk, milk
6. drink, think, shrink
7. e.g. wall, tall, fall, call
8. egg, leg, silk
9. legs, eggs, spiders
10. eyes — legs — silk
11. suck / kill / eat / wrap
12. Spiders are not insects.

UNIT **5** page 16

Maths
1. 8 + 0 = 8
2. 3
3. 2 rows of 3 bees
4. 3 tens
5. The child with the hat.
6. Parent/teacher to check.
7. $1
8. 6
9. elephant
10. Parent/teacher to check.

Answers

11. model on right
12. Parent/teacher to check.
13. e.g. fish bowl, ball
14. Parent/teacher to check.

English

1. 2 pm
2. friend
3. 7
4. 12th March
5. e.g. place, plant, plop, plump, plan
6. daylight, shoelace, photograph
7. excited, happy, surprised, pleased
8. cake, party, present
9. parties, stories, ladies
10. she
11. play, eat
12. How old will Soo Yin be?

UNIT 6 page 18

Maths

1. 15, 14
2. 16
3. Parent/teacher to check.
4. 3 tens
5. chicken
6. 6 strawberries
7. $2
8. 3 o'clock
9. Rob
10. cat on right
11. Parent/teacher to check.
12. square
13. cylinder, sphere
14. Parent/teacher to check.

English

1. peel
2. throw
3. useful
4. Parent/teacher to check.
5. e.g. end, sand, land, pond, tend
6. e.g. sit, hog, fig, dog
7. e.g. stick, pick, sick, click
8. dig, hit, paint
9. hands, balls, oranges
10. My

11. Answers will vary.
12. What can your hands do?

UNIT 7 page 20

Maths

1. 11, 10
2. $18 - 6 = 12$
3. Parent/teacher to check.
4. 20
5. Parent/teacher to check.
6. diamond and square
7. 50c, 20c, 10c
8. Parent/teacher to check.
9. Parent/teacher to check.
10. Parent/teacher to check.
11. bucket
12. middle and left shape
13. block and pyramid
14. Parent/teacher to check.

English

1. plankton
2. fish
3. sea
4. The big fish.
5. shark, fish
6. large, huge, enormous, gigantic
7. e.g. dark, park, spark, lark
8. an, plan, plank, ton, to, on
9. fish, sharks
10. It
11. e.g. eat, swim, chase, catch, chew, hunt
12. I like sharks.

TEST 1 page 22

Maths

1. 20, 13
2. 9; $20 - 6 = 14$
3. Parent/teacher to check.
4. 3, 30
5. Parent/teacher to check.
6. Parent/teacher to check; square, circle
7. 5c, 10c, 20c
8. 8
9. Parent/teacher to check; duck

10. Parent/teacher to check; dog on right
11. 20; 1, 3, 2
12. Parent/teacher to check.
13. Parent/teacher to check.
14. Parent/teacher to check; under

English

1. cartilage
2. people
3. fish
4. If it's hungry, if it mistakes a person for regular food, if it is defending its territory.
5. e.g. stack, lack, dock, click
6. e.g. pat, pit, pin
7. e.g. dish, wish
8. anger, an, us, danger
9. shark, dolphin, turtle, baby
10. they
11. attack/eat, looking/hunting, eat
12. Are sharks interesting creatures?

UNIT 8 page 26

Maths

1. 20, 4
2. $20 - 12 = 8$
3. Parent/teacher to check.
4. 4; 40
5. 7th - seventh, 8th-eight, 9th-ninth
6. circle, square
7. 20c + 20c
8. Parent/teacher to check.
9. Hand print on right.
10. 2, 1, 3
11. 6
12. circle
13. cube, pyramid
14. Parent/teacher to check.

English

1. fried
2. heated
3. ingredient
4. Vegetable Stir Fry

Answers

5. e.g. bread, bright, bring, broccoli
6. bedroom, today, sunlight
7. mango (it's a fruit)
8. broccoli, carrot, corn, onion
9. potatoes, tomatoes
10. pot
11. e.g. cut, eat, chop, cook, wash, chew
12. It's delicious!

UNIT 9 page 28

Maths
1. 20, 1
2. 2, 18
3. 2 rows of 5
4. 3, 7
5. Parent/teacher to check.
6.
7. Parent/teacher to check.
8. 7 o'clock
9. true
10. Parent/teacher to check.
11. more
12. 0, 0
13. cone, sphere
14. above

English
1. bones
2. muscles
3. bread
4. pineapple
5. e.g. cheese, chop, chew
6. pin, apple, pine, nap, pal, pip, pen, leap, nip, lap
7. weak, unlucky, bad
8. to
9. man, woman, child
10. tomato, cheese, chicken, pineapple
11. e.g. eating, tasting, chewing
12. Parent/teacher to check.

UNIT 10 page 30

Maths
1. 10, 10
2. 14, 6

---

3. Parent/teacher to check.
4. 6, 4, 64
5. 2, 4, 6, 8, 10
6. ⬒ $\frac{1}{2}$ ⊕ $\frac{1}{4}$
7. 5c, 10c, 20c
8. Parent/teacher to check.
9. foot
10. tree on right
11. e.g. pool
12. circle
13.
14. in

English
1. share
2. helpful
3. Pashto
4. hurt
5. thing-ring, chalk-talk, stick-thick, day-play
6. important, unhappy or sad, learn
7. friend, Wednesday, knock
8. children, friend, people
9. people, children, friends
10. My
11. e.g. like, help
12. Parent/teacher to check.

UNIT 11 page 32

Maths
1. 15, 14
2. 7, 13
3. Parent/teacher to check.
4. 27, 34, 51
5. 12, 16
6. △ $\frac{1}{2}$ ⊞ $\frac{1}{4}$ ⊕ $\frac{1}{4}$
7. 5c, 20c
8. 2
9.
10. fish on right
11. e.g. cup, jug, bowl
12. Parent/teacher to check.
13. flat, smooth
14. Parent/teacher to check.

English
1. fruit
2. sauce
3. dried
4. Parent/teacher to check.
5. milk
6. rice, oil, bean
7. rice
8. 3, 2, 1
9. noodles, rice, chillies
10. fresh
11. chop, slice, steam, fry, boil, shred
12. Buy apples, oranges, bananas, rice and bread.

UNIT 12 page 34

Maths
1. 20, 20
2. 1, 1
3. Parent/teacher to check.
4. 3, 9, 39
5. 1, 3, 5, 7, 9
6. colour 2 shoes
7. 80c
8. 8
9. Parent/teacher to check.
10. Parent/teacher to check.
11. blocks on left
12. Parent/teacher to check.
13. 6, 5
14. Parent/teacher to check.

English
1. water
2. carry
3. water
4. Answers will vary.
5. spend, day, class
6. their, tried
7. people, heavy, hours
8. lakes, rivers, wells
9. country, person, child
10. waterfall, classroom, playground
11. Fix, Mend
12. All people, plants and animals need water.

Answers

ANSWERS: *Excel* Basic Skills English and Mathematics Year 2

UNIT 13 page 36

Maths
1. 20, 17
2. 13, 12
3. Parent/teacher to check.
4. 73
5. 1, 3, 5, 7, 9, 11, 13, 15, 17, 19
6. Parent/teacher to check.
7. 20c
8. Parent/teacher to check.
9. shape on the right
10. middle face
11. middle and right model
12. 6, 6
13.
14. middle flower

English
1. three
2. five
3. allergic
4. alone
5. this, the, then
6. sting, skin, scrape
7. unhappy, undo, unimportant
8. 1, 2, 3
9. bees, stings, poisons
10.
11. die
12. "It is best to leave bees alone," said Mum.

UNIT 14 page 38

Maths
1. 20, 18
2. 20, 20
3. Parent/teacher to check.
4. 45
5. 20, 40, 60, 80, 100
6. $\frac{1}{4}$
7. $3
8. Parent/teacher to check.
9. false

---

10. Parent/teacher to check.
11. model on the right
12. 13.
14. beside

English
1. eight
2. suckers
3. moray eel
4. It grows back.
5. e.g. crawl, crop, crash, crab
6. e.g. peel, reel, stray
7. e.g. octogon, October, octet
8. eel, octopus, shark
9. boys, eels, enemies
10.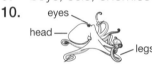
11. fight
12. Parent/teacher to check.

UNIT 15 page 40

Maths
1. 20, 20
2. 10, 8
3. Parent/teacher to check.
4. twenty-five, 25; thirty, 30; thirty-one, 31
5. 92, 81
6. $\frac{1}{2}$
7. piggy bank on right
8. 12:30
9. triangle on left
10. Parent/teacher to check.
11. container on right
12. hexagon, rectangle, diamond
13.
14. Parent/teacher to check.

English
1. fur
2. sleep
3. food
4. prr, yawn, sigh, crunch

---

5. noisily, happily
6. crunch, preen, clean
7. munch, nibble, devour
8. their, flower, sale
9. sheep, deer, salmon
10. Parent/teacher to check.
11. lick, munch, sleep, crunch, rub, tickle
12. Parent/teacher to check.

TEST 2 page 42

Maths
1. 10, 10
2. 20 − 9 = 11, 20 − 12 = 8, 20 − 10 = 10
3. Parent/teacher to check.
4. 2, 4, 24, 42
5. 4, 10, 12, 14, 16, 20, 60, 40, 30
6. square
7. Parent/teacher to check.
8. Parent/teacher to check.
9. Parent/teacher to check.
10. Parent/teacher to check.
11.
12. circle, triangle, square, rectangle
13.
14. Parent/teacher to check.

English
1. cupboard
2. scream
3. wolf
4. Parent/teacher to check.
5. happily, noisily, angrily
6. red, wolf, eat, food
7. e.g. good, hood, could, would
8. sun-son, would-wood, flower-flour, weather-whether
9. girls, days, children, woods
10. He, her
11. screamed, killed, lived
12. "What big ears you have," said Red Riding Hood.

Answers

UNIT 16 page 46

Maths
1. 7, 20
2. 10, 9
3. Parent/teacher to check.
4. twenty, twenty-five
5. 12, 6
6. 1 flower coloured
7. Parent/teacher to check.
8. 3:30
9. three bricks on right
10. Parent/teacher to check.
11. 50 pegs
12.
13. square
14. Parent/teacher to check.

English
1. strangers
2. better
3. Red Riding Hood
4. To listen to her mother's advice; to not talk to strangers.
5. fright, night, sigh, high, sight, delight
6. talk, wolf, path
7. night, sight, light
8. eaten
9. wolves, wives, loaves
10. wolf
11. jump, run, leap, crawl, eat
12. Parent/teacher to check.

UNIT 17 page 48

Maths
1. 20, 19
2. 8, 9
3. Parent/teacher to check.
4. 69
5. 2, 17, 24, 35
6. 1 ice-cream coloured
7. Parent/teacher to check.
8. 7:00
9. $2
10. 2, 3, 1
11. model on the left
12.

---

13. square
14. Parent/teacher to check.

English
1. argued
2. coat
3. hot
4. sun
5. stronger, tighter, hotter
6. e.g. stun, shot, knot
7. e.g. bun, fun, run, gun
8. stronger, harder, tighter
9. roots, cliffs, chefs
10. e.g. hot, shimmering, bright
11. shone, burned
12. "I am stronger," said the sun.

UNIT 18 page 50

Maths
1. 15, 13
2. 14, 16
3. Parent/teacher to check.
4. forty, forty-five
5. 6, 25, 82, 91
6. $\frac{1}{2}$ $\frac{1}{4}$
7. Parent/teacher to check.
8. half past four or four thirty
9. Parent/teacher to check.
10. a pen
11. 2, 1, 3
12. blue, blue, red, red
13. A box's shape.
14. Parent/teacher to check.

English
1. afternoon
2. bend
3. trees
4. fierce, stormy
5. blasting, blustering, blowing
6. afternoon, sunshine, today, thunderstorm
7. whispering, moaning, shrieking, wailing, rustling, crooning, sighing
8. moan, rattle, rustle
9. leaves, knives, loaves

---

10. e.g. fierce, gentle, gusty
11. e.g. blow, push, bully
12. Wind can be gentle or fierce.

UNIT 19 page 52

Maths
1. 18, 16
2. 20, 0
3. Parent/teacher to check.
4. eighty-two, eighty-five
5. 55, 60, 65; 25, 20, 15
6. $\frac{1}{2}$
7. Parent/teacher to check.
8. quarter past three or three fifteen
9. Parent/teacher to check.
10. Parent/teacher to check.
11. 2, 1, 3
12. Parent/teacher to check.
13. square in the middle
14. Parent/teacher to check.

English
1. reptiles
2. chew
3. alone
4. It eats rats and mice.
5. useful, helpful, careful
6. rake, make, cake
7. helpful, handy
8. pray, road, bear
9. snakes, mice, bushes
10. Parent/teacher to check.
11. swallow, squeeze, slide, sleep
12. Parent/teacher to check.

UNIT 20 page 54

Maths
1. 12, 14
2. 10, 10
3. 4, 2
4. 12, 21, 34
5. 24, 26, 28; 48, 50, 52
6. $\frac{1}{4}$
7. $5, $10
8. half past one or one thirty

Answers

9. Parent/teacher to check.
10. Parent/teacher to check.
11. Parent/teacher to check.
12. shape on the left and shape in the middle
13. circle
14. Parent/teacher to check.

English
1. blue
2. dog
3. licorice
4. Aunty Rita
5. ice or rice
6. hard, cake, nose
7. show, know, flow
8. lion, pairs
9. socks, hats, shorts, cakes, noses, claws
10. We
11. buys/gives/sends
12. I wrote a letter to Aunty Rita.

UNIT 21 page 56

Maths
1. 16, 18
2. 7, 6
3. 2
4. 3, 4
5. 2, 4, 6, 8, 10, 12, 14, 16, 18
6. eighths
7. 2, 1, 3
8. Parent/teacher to check.
9. more than 1 fork
10. more than a metre high
11. Parent/teacher to check.
12.

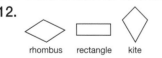
rhombus   rectangle   kite

13. circle
14. Parent/teacher to check.

English
1. puppets
2. science
3. library
4. Parent/teacher to check.
5. sorrow, tomorrow

6. e.g. pots, pats, pans, pant
7. enjoy
8. book, borrow, drama
9. dislike, disappear, disapprove
10. Their, I
11. paint, draw, play, share, make, read, dance, eat
12. Parent/teacher to check.

UNIT 22 page 58

Maths
1. 20, 10
2. Parent/teacher to check.
3. 3
4. 16, 61, 71
5. 5, 10, 15, 20, 25, 30, 35, 40, 45, 50
6. circle and square
7. 20c
8. Parent/teacher to check.
9. Parent/teacher to check.
10. likely
11. The water rises.
12.    13.
14. Parent/teacher to check.

English
1. mammal
2. plants
3. herd
4. Answers will vary e.g. Animals have nowhere to live.
5. e.g. trunk, tree, trace, trap
6. best, pest, test
7. drinking, sniffing, squirting
8. elephant calf, sheep lamb, horse foal
9. bulls, cows, babies
10. cow
11. smelling, drinking
12. Elephants eat tree roots, twigs, leaves and grass.

UNIT 23 page 60

Maths
1. 17, 15

2. Parent/teacher to check.
3. 2, 4, 8
4. 3, 1
5. 79, 89, 97, 99
6. $\frac{2}{4}$ or $\frac{1}{2}$
7. Parent/teacher to check.
8. Parent/teacher to check.
9. 2
10. more than one metre
11. cube, cube
12. Parent/teacher to check.
13. circle
14. Parent/teacher to check.

English
1. pets
2. attention
3. well/properly
4. Parent/teacher to check.
5. taking, choosing, hoping
6. properly
7. e.g. stink, pink, ink, link
8. bird, cat, turtle
9. pet, turtle, bird
10. fish
11. brushed
12. "Hermit crabs are interesting pets," said Jian.

TEST 3 page 62

Maths
1. 18, 17
2. 14, 13
3. Parent/teacher to check.
4. ninety-five, sixty-four
5. 10, 15, 20, 25; 14, 12, 10
6. $\frac{2}{4}$ or $\frac{1}{2}$, 5 balloons
7. Parent/teacher to check.
8. half past four or four thirty
9. 3, 6
10. less than
11. Parent/teacher to check.
12.  and
13. square, circle
14. Parent/teacher to check.

English
1. next door

A6

Answers

2. fence
3. Saturday
4. e.g. happy
5. e.g. when, whether, which, while, what
6. black, white, happy
7. dare, fare, hare, mare
8. fare, tied
9. owners
10. children, fence, dog
11. lived, tied, played
12. "We can share our little dog," she said.

UNIT 24 page 66

Maths
1. 13, 14
2. 18, 11
3. 37
4. 3, 4, 9
5. fifty-nine, 59; ninety-five, 95; fifteen, 15; ninety-nine, 99
6. 2 spotted umbrellas
7. comb, book
8. Friday
9. Parent/teacher check.
10. e.g. desk, gate, shelf
11. bottle
12. rhombus
13. circle
14.

English
1. boar
2. anything
3. animals
4. bacon, pork, ham
5. e.g. field, could, mild, gold
6. cool, grass, sow
7. black, smack, stack
8. piglets, puppies, kittens
9. pigs, sows, boars, piglets, mammals
10. e.g. fat, cute, chubby, clean
11. roll/wallow
12. Parent/teacher to check.

UNIT 25 page 68

Maths
1. 13, 15
2. 10, 11
3. 4 groups of 4
4. 3, 5, 6
5. 80, 50
6. shape on the right
7. yes
8. Parent/teacher to check.
9. 36
10. leaves
11. plate
12. all except triangle
13. rectangle
14. Parent/teacher to check.

English
1. people
2. top
3. campsites, waterholes
4. Parent/teacher to check.
5. drown, gown, frown
6. found, show, tracks
7. down up / curved straight / lost found / show hide
8. k, k, k, b, b
9. dot, circle, line
10. artist, symbol, animals, plant, campsite
11. draw / paint
12. Some Aboriginal artworks look like story maps.

UNIT 26 page 70

Maths
1. 15, 14
2. 50, 30
3. 3, 2, 6
4. 6, 5, 4
5. 15, 12, 9; 36, 34, 32
6. 4 stars
7. Parent/teacher to check.
8. half past ten or ten thirty
9. Parent/teacher to check.
10. Parent/teacher to check.
11. apple
12.

13. circle
14. Parent/teacher to check.

English
1. grandmother
2. wolf
3. Answers will vary.
4. Answers will vary e.g. the girls save themselves; they didn't need rescuing.
5. warning, locking, tricking
6. grandmother, aunt, sister
7. warning, warned, warns
8. lock, grandmother, great
9. girls, sisters, mothers
10. Answers will vary e.g. clever, smart, brave.
11. lock
12. The wolf tricked the girls and they opened the door.

UNIT 27 page 72

Maths
1. 10, 2
2. 60, 70
3. 2, 3, 6
4. 131, 195
5. 13, 23
6. $\frac{1}{2}$ or $\frac{3}{6}$
7. Parent/teacher to check.
8. 11:30
9. 9, 8
10. Parent/teacher to check.
11. Parent/teacher to check.
12. all are symmetrical
13. 8, 12
14. Parent/teacher to check.

English
1. pods
2. blood
3. lungs
4. false
5. e.g. white, when, wheat, whale
6. blood, blow, group
7. e.g. stranger, ranger
8. e.g. too, pool, hoop, cool
9. whales, teeth, babies, lungs, mammals

ANSWERS: *Excel* Basic Skills English and Mathematics Year 2

Answers

10. babies
11. drink
12. "Whales are mammals," said the teacher.

UNIT 28 page 74

Maths

1. 4, 2
2. 3
3. 3, 5, 15
4. one hundred and twenty
5. 10, 35
6. 1 boat
7. Parent/teacher to check.
8. 5:30
9. 1, 3, 2
10. Parent/teacher to check.
11. Parent/teacher to check.
12.
13.
14. Parent/teacher to check.

English

1. red
2. trees
3. fruit
4. nearly extinct, not many left in the wild
5. e.g. back, shark, dark, mark
6. e.g. begs, cat, pan
7. e.g. pale, tale, fail, nail
8. high, long, man
9. apes, rainforests, treetops
10. termites
11. swing
12. Orang-utans eat leaves, bark, fruit, ants and bees.

UNIT 29 page 76

Maths

1. 7, 7
2. 4, 6
3. 4, 3, 12
4. 4, 3, 7
5. 87, 85
6. 2, 6
7. $1

---

8. jump 10 times
9. 18
10. less than a metre
11. banana
12. Parent/teacher to check.
13. cone, sphere
14. Parent/teacher to check.

English

1. seagulls
2. stir-fry
3. Sydney
4. Pop
5. e.g. bottle, kettle, battle, tatty, patted
6. e.g. skilful, clever, excellent, terrific, great, fabulous
7. e.g. hay, stay, may, ray
8. sea
9. chases, chasing, chased.
10. Ben, Pop, Nan, Chi Chu, Sydney
11. ran, chased
12. The Border Collie's name is Ben.

UNIT 30 page 78

Maths

1. 5, 7, 9
2. 2, 4, 9
3. 3 × 4
4. 0, 17, 96, 132
5. 29, 60
6. $\frac{1}{2}$ $\frac{1}{3}$ $\frac{1}{4}$
7. ice-cream and cupcake
8. write my name
9. model on the right
10. Parent/teacher to check.
11. Parent/teacher to check; with a measuring tape or by getting into a bath and measuring the amount the water rises.
12. Parent/teacher to check.
13. Parent/teacher to check.
14. Parent/teacher to check.

English

1. all the time
2. spoil

---

3. night
4. time passes quickly
5. e.g. wrong, wring, wrestle
6. e.g. mend, mind, kind
7. e.g. soon, moon, spoon
8. 1, 3, 2
9. Our Grandmas love us.
10. Grandmas, morning, noon, night, rules
11. e.g. spoil, love, kiss
12. Parent/teacher to check.

TEST 4 page 80

Maths

1. 7, 4, 6
2. 5, 5, 3
3. 3 groups of 5
4. ☆
5. Parent/teacher to check.
6. 1 out of 6, 2 birds
7. 20c, 50c
8. Parent/teacher to check.
9. Parent/teacher to check.
10. Parent/teacher to check.
11. spoon
12. ◐ ⊟ , 🦋
13. 5, 5, 8
14. Parent/teacher to check.

English

1. finger
2. cars
3. fish or rabbit
4. grandpa
5. pit, spit, it
6. policeman, sometimes, forefinger
7. e.g. batch, match, hatch, latch
8. piece, rode, one
9. farmers, rabbits, supplies, food
10. From: farmer, chaff, horse, sulky, boy, family, Dad, policeman, cars
11. tied, wrapped; ate, bit
12. "My grandfather's name is Eric," said Robert.

9

Colour a shape to cover 15 squares.

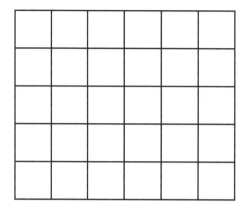

10

Trace the shortest path to the carrot.

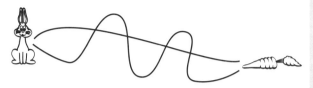

Draw a face with longer hair.

11

Circle the model that uses the least blocks.

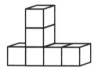

GEOMETRY **12**

Name the shapes.

 _____

 _____

_____

 _____

13

Colour the shapes which will roll and tick the shapes which will stack.

 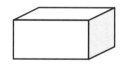

14

Help the spider reach the fly.

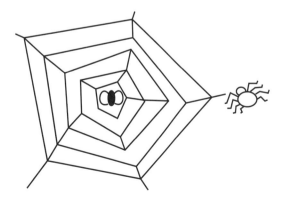

Playscript: Little Red Riding Hood

<u>Narrator</u>: Little Red Riding Hood had to walk through the woods to take a basket of food to her grandmother. Her mother warned her to stay on the path and not to talk to strangers. On the way she met a wolf.

<u>Little Red Riding Hood</u>: Hello sir.

<u>Wolf</u>: Where are you going?

<u>Little Red Riding Hood</u>: I'm taking this basket of food to my grandmother. She lives on the other side of the woods.

<u>Wolf</u>: What a kind girl you are. On your way, then.

<u>Little Red Riding Hood</u>: Goodbye.

<u>Narrator</u>: Little Red Riding Hood continued on her way to her grandmother's house. Meanwhile the wolf had raced ahead of her. He tied up the grandmother and hid her in a cupboard. Then he put on a hat and glasses and hopped into bed. There was a knock on the door.

<u>Wolf</u>: Come in my dear.

<u>Little Red Riding Hood</u>: Why grandmother, what big ears you have.

<u>Wolf</u>: All the better to hear you with, my dear.

<u>Little Red Riding Hood</u>: Why grandmother, what big eyes you have.

<u>Wolf</u>: All the better to see you with, my dear.

<u>Little Red Riding Hood</u>: Why grandmother, what big teeth you have.

<u>Wolf</u>: All the better to eat you with, my dear.

<u>Narrator</u>: Little Red Riding Hood screamed. A passing woodcutter heard her and came running to her rescue. He killed the wolf and untied grandmother and they all lived happily ever after—except the wolf.

---

1 READING & COMPREHENSION

The wolf hid the grandmother in the (cupboard / dishwasher / bed).

2

The woodcutter heard Red Riding Hood (whisper / scream / laugh).

3

Everyone lived happily ever after except the _____ .

4 What would you have done if you were Red Riding Hood?

_____

English

5

Add the ending *ly* to these words.

happy _____   noisy _____   angry _____

6

Unscramble the letters to make words from the play.

der _____   lfwo _____   tae _____   oodf _____

7

Write three words that rhyme with *wood*.

_____   _____   _____

8

Link the pairs of homophones.

sun	whether
wood	son
flower	would
weather	flour

9

Write the plurals.

girl _____   day _____

child _____   wood _____

10

Replace the nouns in the sentence with pronouns.

The woodcutter rescued Red Riding Hood.   _____ rescued _____ .

11

Complete the sentences with verbs.

Red Riding Hood _____ . The woodchopper

_____ the wolf. Grandma _____ happily ever after.

12

Speech marks (" ") are used to show what a person says. Write the sentence correctly.

what big ears you have said red riding hood

_____

Mathematics

NUMBER

1

$13 + \boxed{} = 20$

$7 + 13 = \boxed{}$

2

$15 - 5 = \boxed{}$

$15 - 6 = \boxed{}$

3 Draw 3 groups of 3 apples.

4 Write the words.

20 _____

25 _____

5 What number comes next?

a) 18, 16, 14, ____

b) 15, 12, 9, ____

6 Colour one eighth of the flowers.

7 Circle the coins needed to buy an apple for 50c.

MEASUREMENT

8 Which shows half past 3? Tick it.

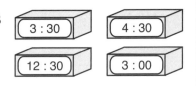

9 Circle the pile which would be heavier.

10 Trace the shortest path from the rabbit to the carrot.

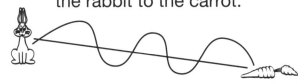

11 Estimate and match.

 holds

50 pegs

400 pegs

12 pegs

GEOMETRY

12 Colour the hexagon.

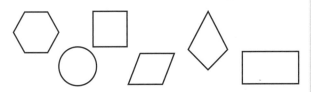

13 What shape is each face—square, triangle or circle?

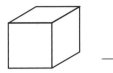

_____

14 Draw a cat between the trees.

Dear Diary

I had an awful fright today. A nasty wolf pretended to be my grandmother and I was nearly eaten. I was really scared but a woodcutter came and killed the wolf. I am never going to wander off the path through the woods again. I should have followed my mother's advice to stay on the path and not talk to strangers. I've learnt my lesson. Grandma is going to stay with us until she has recovered from her fright.

READING & COMPREHENSION

1 Mum said not to talk to (wolves / strangers / grandmothers).

2 Grandma is staying until she is (better / sick / eaten).

3 The diary belongs to

_____ .

4 What lesson did Red Riding Hood learn? _____

_____

SPELLING & VOCABULARY

5 Circle words with the spelling pattern *igh*.

fright, night, sigh, high, rely, spy, sight, delight

6 Unscramble the words from the story.

kalt _____   flow _____   phat _____

7 List words which rhyme with *fright*.

n _____   s _____   l _____

8 Cross out the incorrect words.

Red Riding Hood was nearly (eat / eaten / eating) by the wolf.

9 Change *f* to *v* to make plurals.

wolf _____   wife _____   loaf _____

GRAMMAR & PUNCTUATION

10 Choose a noun from the box that fits the group.

fox, dog, dingo, _____

lion, tiger, wolf, panther

11 Circle the verbs for actions that a wolf can do.

jump, run, leap, fly, crawl, laugh, giggle, eat, drive, knit

12 Answer with a sentence. Do you think Red Riding Hood has learnt a lesson? _____

Mathematics

1

$$19 + 1 = \boxed{}$$

$$1 + \boxed{} = 20$$

2

$$16 - 8 = \boxed{}$$

$$17 - 8 = \boxed{}$$

3 Draw 2 groups of 4 mice.

4 Write the number that is

6 tens and 9 ones.

_____

5 Write the numbers in order
from smallest to largest.

24, 2, 35, 17

_____ , _____ , _____ , _____

6 Colour $\frac{1}{4}$ of the ice-creams.

7 Circle the coins you would use
to buy an ice cream for $1.00 .

8 Match.

7 : 00   9 : 30

8 : 00   9 : 00

9 Colour the coin with the
smallest area.

10 Number the lines in order from
shortest to longest.

_____

_____

_____

11 Circle the model with the
largest volume.

12 Colour the curved
shapes blue.

13 A cereal box would have:

square faces ____

triangle faces ____

14 Draw a vase on the top shelf.

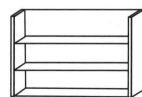

Playscript: Who Is Stronger?

<u>Narrator:</u> The wind and the sun were arguing about who was stronger.

<u>Wind:</u> I am stronger than you and I will prove it. I will get that man's coat off.

<u>Narrator:</u> The wind raged and howled trying to get the man's coat off but the harder the wind blew, the tighter the man held onto his coat.

<u>Sun:</u> I can get the man's coat off. Watch this.

<u>Narrator:</u> The sun burned down. The man grew hot and took off his coat.

<u>Sun:</u> You see, I am stronger than you.

1   READING & COMPREHENSION

The sun and the wind (agreed / argued / angered).

2

The man held onto his (clothes / coat / hat).

3

The man took off his coat because the sun was so _____ .

4 Who was stronger—the wind or the sun?

_____

---

5   SPELLING & VOCABULARY

Add *er* to each word.

strong _____   tight _____   hot(t) _____

6 Add one letter to make new words.

sun   s __ u n   hot   ___ h o t   not   ___ n o t

7 List words which rhyme with *sun*.

_____

8 Add the suffix *er* to the adjectives.

strong_____   hard_____   tight_____

9 Add *s* to make plurals.

roof _____   cliff _____   chef _____

10   GRAMMAR & PUNCTUATION

Write three adjectives to describe the sun.

_____   _____   _____

11 Complete the sentence with a verb.

The sun _____ onto the man.

12 Write the sentence correctly.   i am stronger said the sun

_____

1 NUMBER

$2 + 3 +$ ⬜ $= 20$

$3 +$ ⬜ $+ 4 = 20$

2

$20 - 6 =$ ⬜

$20 - 4 =$ ⬜

3 Draw 2 groups of 6 dots.

4 Write the words.

40 _____

45 _____

5 Write the numbers in order from smallest to largest.

25, 91, 82, 6

____ , ____ , ____ , ____

6 Link:

$\frac{1}{2}$

$\frac{1}{4}$

7 Draw the coins needed to buy an orange for 50c.

8 MEASUREMENT

Write the time in words.

 4 : 30

_____

9 Draw something heavier than a pencil.

10 Which is longer:

a pin? ____

a pen? ____

11 Number the models in order from the smallest to largest volume.

12 GEOMETRY Trace the curved lines in red and the straight lines in blue.

13 This shape folds to make:

a box ____

a bowl ____

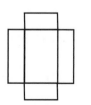

14 Draw a book on the bottom shelf.

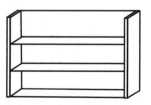

50

Wind

Gentle breezes
arrive with the morning
tickling the trees, nudging the leaves,
rustling, whispering, crooning, sighing.

Gusty squalls
arrive through the afternoon
pushing the trees, rattling the leaves,
blowing, shoving, bullying, moaning.

Fierce storms
arrive in the evening
blasting the trees, ripping the leaves,
blustering, gusting, shrieking, wailing
forcing the trees to bend in its path.

1 Gusty squalls arrive through the (morning / afternoon / night).

2 The wind forces trees to (bend / grow / push).

3 Gentle breezes tickle the

_____ .

4 What kind of wind blasts the trees and rips the leaves?

_____

5 Find three words in the poem that start with *bl*.

_____   _____   _____

6 Link words to make compound words.

after   sun   noon   to   shine   day   thunder   storm

7 Write three words from the poem that tell the noise the wind makes.

_____   _____   _____

8 Write the words in alphabetical order.

rattle, rustle, moan _____

9 Change *f* to *v* to make plurals.

leaf _____   knife _____   loaf _____

10 Write three adjectives to describe different kinds of wind.

_____   _____   _____

11 Write three verbs for actions that the wind can do.

_____   _____   _____

12 Write the sentence correctly.   wind can be gentle or fierce

_____

NUMBER

1

9 + 9 = ☐

8 + 8 = ☐

2

20 − 0 = ☐

20 − 20 = ☐

3 Draw 2 groups of 8 forks.

4 Write the words.

82 _____

85 _____

5 Write the next 3 numbers.

40, 45, 50, ___ , ___ , ___

40, 35, 30, ___ , ___ , ___

6 What fraction of the balloons are coloured?

____

7 Draw the coins you would use to buy a comb for $2.00 .

MEASUREMENT

8 Write the time in words.

 3 : 15

_____

9 Draw something lighter than your shoe.

10 Use hand spans to measure the length of your desk.

My desk is _____ hand spans long.

11 Number the models in order from smallest to largest volume.

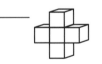

GEOMETRY

12 Trace the broken line in yellow and the zig-zag line in blue.

13 Circle the shape of 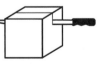 the cross section.

 ☐ ☐

14 Colour the joey's path to its mother.

Snakes

Snakes are reptiles like lizards, turtles and crocodiles. Snakes have scales. Snakes don't have eyelids so they can't blink. Their eyes are covered by a transparent scale.

Snakes swallow their prey whole without chewing. Sometimes their prey is alive when it is swallowed.

Snakes are useful in the country because they eat rats and mice which can destroy farmers' crops. People should be careful when walking in the bush and should leave snakes alone. A snake will normally only bite a person if it feels threatened.

1 Snakes are (lizards / crocodiles / reptiles).

2 Snakes don't (chew / swallow / digest) their food.

3 People should leave snakes _____ .

4 How is a snake useful?

_____

_____

5 Add the suffix *ful* to these words.

use _____   help _____   care _____

6 Write words that rhyme with *snake*.

r _____   m _____   c _____

7 Underline the words that mean *useful*.

helpful, handy, hurtful, useless

8 Write homophones for these words.

prey _____   rode _____   bare _____

9 Write the plurals.

snake _____   mouse _____   bush _____

10 Draw a picture of a snake and label it with nouns.

11 Circle the verbs for actions that a snake can do.

swallow, squeeze, run, slide, sleep, chew, hop

12 Answer with a sentence.   How do you feel about snakes?

_____

Mathematics

1 NUMBER

6 + 6 = ☐

7 + 7 = ☐

2

17 − 7 = ☐

19 − 9 = ☐

3

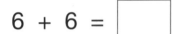

☐ groups of ☐ crosses.

4

Write in sequence from smallest to largest.

21, 34, 12

____ , ____ , ____

5

Write the next 3 numbers.

18, 20, 22, ___ , ___ , ___

42, 44, 46, ___ , ___ , ___

6

What fraction of the fish are coloured?

 ____

7

Label the notes.

8 MEASUREMENT

Write the time in words.

_____

9

Draw a shape with a larger area.

10

Use an object of your choice to measure the length of your desk. My desk is

_____ long.

11

Draw a model with a larger volume.

12 GEOMETRY

Circle the closed shapes.

13

Colour the label for the cross-section of the shape.

(Rectangle)   (Circle)

(Triangle)   (Square)

14

Colour the path for the koala to reach its tree.

Dear Aunty Rita,
Thank you for my birthday present. I really like the shorts and the hat, and blue is my favourite colour. I received some great presents for my birthday. I got a basketball, three books, two pairs of socks, some undies, a torch, glow stickers and coloured pencils. Dad made my birthday cake. It was shaped like a dog. It had licorice for its nose, eyes and claws. Next year I've asked Dad for a lion cake. He says that might be too hard because he doesn't know how to do the lion's mane.
Love, you know who   xxxooxxxoo

READING & COMPREHENSION

1 The birthday shorts are (red / blue / yellow).

2 The birthday cake was shaped like a (lion / dog / basketball).

3 The nose on the cake was made out of _____ .

4 Who bought the shorts and hat?
_____

SPELLING & VOCABULARY

5 Can you find a word inside *licorice*?
Write it. _____

6 Unscramble the words from the story.
hrad _____   kace _____   nseo _____

7 Write the words that rhyme with *glow*.
sh _____   kn _____   fl _____

8 Cross out the incorrect words.
I want a (lion / loin / line) cake. I got two (pears / pairs) of socks.

9 Find six plural words in: sockshatsshortscakesnosesclaws.
_____

GRAMMAR & PUNCTUATION

10 Circle the correct pronoun.
<u>Dad and I</u> will make a lion cake. (They / Them / We / Us)

11 Complete the sentence with a verb.
Aunty Rita _____ great presents.

12 Write the sentence correctly.   i wrote a letter to aunty rita
_____

Mathematics

NUMBER

1

8 + 8 = ☐

9 + 9 = ☐

2

14 − 7 = ☐

14 − 8 = ☐

3

3 groups of ☐ crosses.

4

34

How many tens? _____

How many ones? _____

5

Write the even numbers up to 20.

_____

_____

6

Is this shape cut into quarters, halves or eighths?

_____

7

Number the notes in order of value from least to most.

_____   _____   _____

MEASUREMENT

8

Show quarter past five.

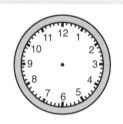

9

A book is as heavy as:

1 fork _____

more than 1 fork _____

10

Tick the correct answer.
The doorway is:

about a metre high _____

less than a metre high _____

more than a metre high _____

11

Draw a model with a smaller volume.

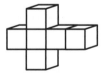

GEOMETRY

12

Link the shape to its label.

rectangle   kite   rhombus

13

Colour the label for the cross section.

(Diamond)   (Square)

(Circle)   (Triangle)

14

Draw a child upside down.

English

School

School is a really good place to go because there are lots of things to do and lots of things to learn about.

My favourite subjects are drama and science. I like drama because we make up plays. We also make puppets. It's lots of fun. I like science because we learn about living things such as insects and caterpillars. I also like learning about ways to care for the environment.

My class goes to the library every week and we get to borrow books. I read in bed every night.

READING & COMPREHENSION

1 In drama you can play with (equipment / puppets / paint).

2 We learn about the environment in (subjects / insects / science).

3 Books are borrowed from the

_____ .

4 What is your favourite school subject and why? _____

_____

SPELLING & VOCABULARY

5 Complete these words that rhyme with *borrow*.

s _____   tom _____

6 Change one letter at a time to make a new word.

lots, p _____ , _____ , _____ , _____

7 Synonyms are words with similar meanings. Circle a synonym for *like*.

detest   enjoy   hate   fun

8 Write the words in alphabetical order.

drama, borrow, book _____

9 Add the prefix *dis* to make antonyms.

like _____like   appear _____appear   approve _____approve

GRAMMAR & PUNCTUATION

10 Choose the correct pronouns.

(I / Him / Their) favourite subject is spelling. (I / My / Their) like science.

11 Circle the verbs you can do at school.

paint, draw, art, play, drama, share, make, read, sleep, eat, dance

12 Answer with a sentence.   What is the name of your school?

_____

NUMBER

1

$10 + 10 =$ ☐

$4 + 6 +$ ☐ $= 20$

2
Draw pictures to show
$15 - 6 = 9$

3

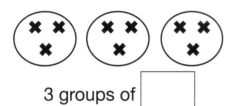

3 groups of ☐

4
Write in sequence from smallest to largest.

61, 16, 71

_____ , _____ , _____

5
Count by 5s to 50. Write the numbers.

_____

_____

6
Circle the shapes that show quarters.

MEASUREMENT

7
A juice costs 80c. I have $1.00. How much change will I get?

_____

8
Write what you do at this time of the night.

_____

9
Draw a footprint with a greater area.

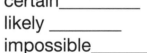

10
Estimate and tick one answer.
It will rain some time during the year.

certain_____

likely _____

impossible_____

11 Describe what happens when you place a rock in a container of water.

_____

_____

GEOMETRY

12
Draw the mirror half.

13
Draw the shape of the cross section.

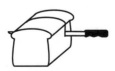

14
Help the mouse find the cheese.

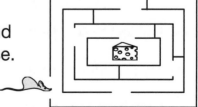

Elephants

Elephants are mammals. They live in herds of up to 40 members. Male elephants are called bulls and females are called cows. Baby elephants are called calves.

Elephants eat tree roots, twigs, leaves and grass. The trunk is actually the elephant's nose. Elephants stick their trunks in the air to sniff out danger. They also use their trunks for drinking. They suck the water up their trunk and then squirt it into their mouths.

Elephants are endangered due to hunting and loss of habitat.

READING & COMPREHENSION

1 An elephant is a
(herd / bull / mammal).

2 Elephants eat
(plants / meat / fish).

3 An elephant group is called a
_____ .

4 What does *loss of habitat* mean?
_____ .

SPELLING & VOCABULARY

5 Write three words that start with *tr*.

_____   _____   _____

6 Write words that rhyme with *rest*.

b _____   p _____   t _____

7 Add *ing* to the words.

drink _____   sniff _____   squirt _____

8 Link the parents with their babies.

elephant   horse   sheep   lamb   foal   calf

9 Write the plurals.

bull _____   cow _____   baby _____

GRAMMAR & PUNCTUATION

10 Use a noun to complete the sentence.

A female elephant is called a _____ .

11 Choose a verb to complete the sentence.

Elephants use their trunk for _____ .

12 Answer with a sentence.   What do elephants eat?

_____

Mathematics

1
NUMBER

9 + 8 = ▢

7 + 8 = ▢

2
Draw pictures to show

20 − 5 = 15

3
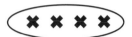

How many groups? _____
How many in each group? _____
How many crosses altogether? _____

4
31

How many tens? _____

How many ones? _____

5
Write the numbers in order
from smallest to largest.

99, 89, 97, 79

_____ , _____ , _____ , _____

6
What fraction of the
elephants are coloured? _____

7
Draw the coins needed to buy
an eraser for 60c.

8
MEASUREMENT

Write what you do
at this time of the
morning.

_____

9

1 book is as heavy as _____ oranges.

10
Estimate and tick one answer.
My room is:
more than 1 metre long _____
less than 1 metre long _____
about 1 metre long _____

11
Which object made the water
rise the most? _____
Which object has the most
volume?

_____

12
GEOMETRY
Draw lines to finish
the shapes.

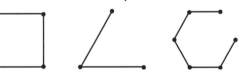

13
Draw the
shape of
the cross
section.

14
Help the bird
find its nest.

The Best Pet

Many people have pets. Some people believe that dogs make good pets. Other people think that cats make the best pets. Some people prefer fish. Some people like birds. Choosing the right pet for you is very important. For example, you need to think about how much of your time the pet needs. Some pets, like dogs, need lots of looking after and lots of attention. Other pets, like turtles, don't need very much looking after at all. Whatever kind of pet you have, you must look after it properly.

1 Many people have (pets / time / things).

2 Some pets need lots of (attention / fish / brushing).

3 You must look after your pet

_____ .

4 What kind of pet do you like best?

_____

5 Add the suffix *ing* to each word.

take _____   choose _____   hope _____

6 Cross out the incorrect word.

Look after your pet (properly / property).

7 Write some words that rhyme with *think*.

_____

8 Write the words in alphabetical order.

turtle, bird, cat _____

9 Write the singular.

pets _____   turtles _____   birds_____

10 Choose the correct noun.

A (cat / dog / fish / rabbit) has no fur.

11 Complete the sentence with a verb.

Dogs with long fur need to be _____ regularly.

12 Write the sentence correctly.   hermit crabs are interesting pets said jian

_____

Mathematics

1

NUMBER

$$9 + 9 = \boxed{}$$

$$13 + 4 = \boxed{}$$

2

$$20 - 6 = \boxed{}$$

$$20 - 7 = \boxed{}$$

3

Draw 2 rows of 4 fish.

4

Write the words.

95 _____

64 _____

5

Fill in the missing numbers.

5, ___ , ___ , ___ , ___ , 30

20, 18, 16, ___ , ___ , ___

6

What part of the shape is coloured? 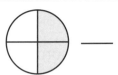 —

Colour one half of the balloons.

7

Draw the coins needed to buy an ice-cream for 80c.

MEASUREMENT

8

Write the time in words.

_____

9

1 book is as heavy as _____ apples.

Estimate:

2 books are as heavy as _____ apples.

10

My shoe is

(less than / more than /

about the same as)

a metre long.

11

Draw a model with
a greater volume.

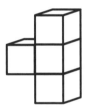

12

GEOMETRY

Continue the
pattern by sliding the shape.

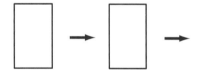

Continue the pattern by
turning the shape.

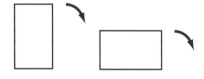

13

Draw the shapes of
the cross-sections.

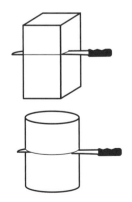

14

Colour the path for the baby
elephant to reach its mother.

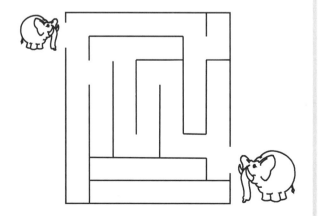

The Lucky Dog

The little black and white dog was tied to the fence all day while its owners went to work. It didn't have anyone to play with but it was a very good dog and it would sit quietly all day long waiting for its owners to come home. Then it would jump and hop and roll onto its back and kick its legs with excitement.

One day two children moved into the house next door. They saw the little black and white dog tied to the fence. They felt sorry for it so they climbed the fence and played with it all that day and all the next day. The little black and white dog was so happy.

The next day was Saturday. The owners of the little black and white dog did not go to work on Saturday so they were at home when the two children climbed the fence to play with the dog. They saw how happy their dog was and how happy the two children were and they felt guilty about leaving their little dog tied to the fence every day. They said to the children, "We can share our little dog and he can have four owners—two owners for during the week and two owners for the weekends."

After that the little black and white dog lived happily ever after and he never had to be tied to the fence again.

---

1 READING & COMPREHENSION

The children lived (with the dog / next door / down the street).

2

The children climbed the (house / fence / dog).

3

The people did not work on _____ .

4

How does the little dog feel at the end of the text?

_____

5 *White* starts with *wh*. Write three other words that start with *wh*.

_____ _____ _____

6 Unscramble the words from the story.

backl _____ hwtie _____ ppyha _____

7 Write words that rhyme with *share*.

d _____ f _____ h _____ m _____

8 Cross out the incorrect words.

I paid my bus (fair / fare). The dog was (tired / tied) to the fence.

9 Complete the sentence with a plural noun.

The little dog now has four _____ .

10 Underline the three nouns in the sentence.

The two children climbed the fence to play with the little dog.

11 Complete the sentences with verbs.

The little dog _____ happily ever after. The little dog was not

_____ to the fence any more. The children _____
with the dog.

12 Write the sentence correctly.
we can share our little dog she said

_____

Mathematics

1 — NUMBER

6 + 7 = ☐

6 + 8 = ☐

2

18 − 0 = ☐

16 − 5 = ☐

3
What number does the
tally represent?

_____

4
36 = ☐ tens   41 = ☐ tens

98 = ☐ tens

5
Link: fifty-nine   99

ninety-five   95

fifteen   59

ninety-nine   15

6
Draw spots on half the umbrellas.

7
I have a $5.00 note and a $1.00 coin. Circle the things I could buy.

 $10.00 $1.00  $3.00

8 — MEASUREMENT
If 14 May is a Wednesday,
what day of the week is 16 May?

_____

9
Name something heavier than you.

_____

10
Name 2 things that are
about 1 metre long.

1. _____

2. _____

11
Jug = 6 cups
Bottle = 5 cups

The _____ has
the lesser capacity.

12 — GEOMETRY
This shape is a
(rhombus/ cube/ rectangle).

13
Draw the shape you would see
from the top.

14
Draw this model from the top.

66

Pigs

Pigs are mammals. A male pig is called a boar and a female pig is called a sow. Pigs can be brown, black, spotted, white or ginger. They are very clean animals. They like to wallow in mud because it helps to keep them cool in hot weather.

Pigs can eat anything. They eat meat, grains, vegetables, fruit, grass and roots. Some scientists believe that pigs are very intelligent—even smarter than dogs. Pigs are killed so that people can eat their meat. Bacon and pork are meats that come from pigs.

READING & COMPREHENSION

1 A male pig is called a (sow / boar / piglet).

2 Pigs eat (meat / fruit / anything).

3 Pigs are very clean

_____

4 What sort of meat do people get from pigs?

_____

SPELLING & VOCABULARY

5 Write three words that end in *ld* like *build*.

_____   _____   _____

6 Unscramble the words from the text.

loco _____   sgars _____   wos _____

7 Write the words.

bl + ack _____   sm + ack _____   st + ack _____

8 What are the babies of these animals called?

pigs _____   dogs _____   cats _____

9 Find five plural words in: pigssowsboarspigletsmammals

_____

GRAMMAR & PUNCTUATION

10 Write three adjectives to describe pigs.

_____   _____   _____

11 Complete the sentence with a verb.

Pigs like to _____ in the mud.

12 Answer with a sentence.   What would you name a pet pig?

_____

Mathematics

1 | NUMBER | **2**

$7 + 6 = \boxed{}$

$7 + 8 = \boxed{}$

$17 - 7 = \boxed{}$

$19 - 8 = \boxed{}$

3

Colour the correct one.

(4 groups of 2)   (4 groups of 4)

4

$34 = \boxed{}$ tens $53 = \boxed{}$ tens

$62 = \boxed{}$ tens

5

Fill in the missing numbers.

100, 90, _____ , 70,

60, _____ , 40

6

Colour the shape or shapes which show thirds.

7

I want to buy two bread rolls for $1.20. Do I have enough money?

Yes _____
No _____

8 | MEASUREMENT

Show: (7 : 30)

9

How many triangles make up this shape?

_____

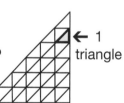 ← 1 triangle

10

Circle the two objects which are the same length.

11

What has the greater volume —a cup or a plate?

_____

12 | GEOMETRY

Circle the shapes which show a line of symmetry.

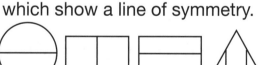

13

Match the object with its top view.

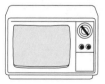

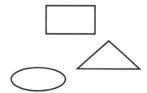

14

Draw the hand from the top view.

Signs and Symbols

Aboriginal artists often use symbols to draw places, plants, animals and events. Artists draw the symbols using patterns of dots, circles and curved and straight lines. Often the symbols are drawn looking down onto them. This is called an aerial view.

Human footprints represent people travelling though a country.

Animal tracks show which animals can be found in an area. Some symbols show places such as campsites and waterholes.

READING & COMPREHENSION

1 Artists use footprints to show (people / campsites / waterholes).

2 An aerial view shows a view from the (side / bottom / top).

3 What places could be shown in Aboriginal art?_____ .

4 Draw how you would show snake tracks near a waterhole.

SPELLING & VOCABULARY

5 Write rhyming words for *down*.

dr_____   g_____   fr_____

6 Change one letter to make a word from the text.

sound _____   shop _____   trucks _____

7 Link the antonyms.

down   show   found   lost   curved   hide   straight   up

8 Circle the silent letters.

knot   knit   knife   climb   comb

9 Write the singular form of these nouns.

dots _____   circles _____   lines _____

GRAMMAR & PUNCTUATION

10 Circle the nouns.

artist   symbol   look   draw   animals   plants   campsite   painted

11 Complete the sentence with a verb.

Artists _____ animals, plants and places that are important to them.

12 Write the sentence correctly.   some aboriginal artworks look like story maps _____

Mathematics

NUMBER

1

$9 + 6 =$ ☐

$9 + 5 =$ ☐

2

$100 - 50 =$ ☐

$100 - 70 =$ ☐

3

How many groups? _____

How many in each group? _____

How many altogether? _____

4

654

How many hundreds? _____

How many tens? _____

How many ones? _____

5

Write the next 3 numbers.

a) 24, 21, 18, ___ , ___ , ___

b) 42, 40, 38, ___ , ___ , ___

6

Colour one half of the stars.

☆ ☆ ☆

☆ ☆ ☆ ☆ ☆

7

Colour coins to make $2.00 .

MEASUREMENT

8

Write the
time in words.

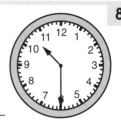

_____

9

Name something lighter than you.

_____

10

Trace the **perimeter** of
the rectangle in red.

11 Which has the greater volume—
an apple or a peg? _____

GEOMETRY

12 Draw a line of symmetry
through each shape.

☐ ◯

13 Colour the correct top view
for the object.

☐ ◯ △

14 Draw from the side.

Book Review

Lon Po Po by Ed Young

'Lon Po Po' is a Chinese story. It's similar to 'Little Red Riding Hood'.

In 'Lon Po Po', three sisters stay at home while their mother goes to visit their grandmother. The mother warns the girls to lock the door and not let anyone in. The wolf arrives disguised as the grandmother. He tricks the girls and they let him into the house. When the oldest sister realises he is a wolf she outsmarts him. This is a great story. I like the way the wolf is tricked in the end.

READING & COMPREHENSION

1 The wolf is disguised as a (mother / grandmother / girl).

2 The girls let the (wolf / grandmother / mother) into the house.

3 'Lon Po Po' is similar to 'Red Riding Hood' because

_____

4 'Lon Po Po' is different from 'Red Riding Hood' because

_____

SPELLING & VOCABULARY

5 Write these words with the suffix *ing*.

warn_____ lock_____ trick_____

6 Circle the words for females.

grandmother   father   brother   aunt   uncle   sister   grandfather

7 Add *ing*, *ed* and *s* to the word *warn*.

_____   _____   _____

8 Write the words in alphabetical order.

lock   great   grandmother _____

9 Unscramble the plural words from the text.

glris _____   tisssre _____   thsmore _____

GRAMMAR & PUNCTUATION

10 Write an adjective on the line.

The _____ girls outsmarted the wolf.

11 Complete the sentence with a verb.

The mother said, "_____ the door".

12 Use *and* to join the two sentences into one. The wolf tricked the girls. They opened the door. _____

Mathematics

NUMBER

1

$$9 + 4 = 3 + \boxed{}$$

$$9 + 3 = 10 + \boxed{}$$

2

$$100 - 40 = \boxed{}$$

$$100 - 30 = \boxed{}$$

3

How many groups? _____

How many in each group? _____

How many altogether? _____

4

Write in numerals.

one hundred and thirty-one _____

one hundred and ninety-five _____

5

What comes next?

a) 19, 17, 15, _____

b) 29, 27, 25, _____

6

What fraction of
the boats are not coloured? _____

7

Colour coins to make $2.00.

MEASUREMENT

8

Show half
past eleven.

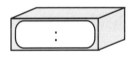

9

How many squares make
up the shapes?

 _____   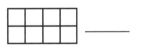 _____

10

Use a pen to measure the
perimeter of your desk.
My desk has a perimeter of

_____ pen lengths.

11

Name an object that has a
volume less than a banana.

_____

GEOMETRY

12

Colour the
symmetrical shapes.

13

 How many corners? _____

How many edges? _____

14

Draw the face from the front.

Whales

Whales are mammals. They have warm blood and they breathe air through their blowholes into their lungs. Female whales give birth to live babies underwater and help the babies come to the surface to breathe air as soon as they are born. Baby whales drink their mother's milk. Whales travel in groups called pods. These vary in size from 5 to 1000 whales depending on the species of whale. Whales in a pod help each other find food and they help to protect each other from danger. Some whale species are endangered.

READING & COMPREHENSION

1 Whales travel in
(pods / species / mammals).

2 Whales have warm
(food / blood / breath).

3 Whales breathe air into their

_____ .

4 True or false? Whales lay eggs.

_____

SPELLING & VOCABULARY

5 Write three words that start with _wh_.

_____ _____ _____

6 Write the words.

bl + ood _____ bl + ow _____ gr + oup _____

7 Write two words that rhyme with _danger_.

str _____ r _____

8 Write two words that have the letters _oo_ in them.

_____ _____

9 Write the plural words you find in: whalesteethbabieslungsmammals

_____

GRAMMAR & PUNCTUATION

10 Complete the sentence with a noun.

Female whales give birth to live _____ .

11 Complete the sentence with a verb.

Whale babies _____ milk.

12 Write the sentence correctly.   whales are mammals said the teacher

_____

1 NUMBER

$9 + 5 = 10 + \boxed{}$

$6 + 6 = 10 + \boxed{}$

2

$$\begin{array}{r} 9 \\ -\ 6 \\ \hline \end{array}$$

3

(✗ ✗ ✗ ✗ ✗) (✗ ✗ ✗ ✗ ✗) (✗ ✗ ✗ ✗ ✗)

How many groups? _____

How many in each group? _____

How many altogether? _____

4

Write this number in words.

120 _____

_____

5

Fill in the missing numbers.

a) 25, 20, 15, _____

b) 50, 45, 40, _____

6

Colour $\frac{1}{3}$ of the boats.

7

Colour coins to make $2.00.

8 MEASUREMENT

Match the clocks.

5 : 30

6 : 30

7 : 30

9

Number the objects in order from lightest to heaviest.

 _____ _____ _____

10

Use a pencil to measure the length of your arm.

How many pencil lengths long is your arm? _____

11

Name an object that has a volume greater than an orange.

_____

12 GEOMETRY

Repeat the patterns.

◇ ○ ◇ ○ __ __

○ ☐ ○ ☐ __ __ __ __

13

Colour the shapes which have only flat surfaces.

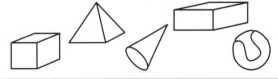

14

Help the child get home.

Orang-utans

Orang-utans are apes which live in the rainforests of Sumatra and Borneo. The name *orang-utan* means 'man of the forest'. Orang-utans have long, red-coloured hair.

Orang-utans use their arms to swing from branch to branch in the rainforest. They build nests high in the treetops to sleep. The orang-utan's favourite food is fruit. They also eat bark, leaves, ants, termites and bees.

Orang-utans are an endangered species.

1 Orang-utans have
(red / brown / black) hair.

2 Orang-utans nest in
(trees / caves / burrows).

3 _____ is the
orang-utan's favourite food.

4 What does *endangered* mean?
_____
_____

5 Fill in the middle letters.

b ___ ___ k   sh ___ ___ k   d ___ ___ k   m ___ ___ k

6 Change a letter to make a new word.

bees   be ___ s   eat   ___ at   man   ___ an

7 Write two words that rhyme with *male*.

_____   _____

8 Find antonyms in the text for these words.

low _____   short _____   woman _____

9 Write the plurals for these nouns.

ape _____   rainforest _____   treetop _____

10 Choose a noun from the box to match the group.

bees, ants, _____

termites, bark, orang-utans

11 Complete the sentence with a verb.

Orang-utans _____ from branch to branch.

12 Write the sentence correctly.   orang-utans eat leaves bark fruit ants
and bees _____

Mathematics

NUMBER

1

$$\begin{array}{r} 2 \\ + 5 \\ \hline \end{array}$$

$$\begin{array}{r} 3 \\ + 4 \\ \hline \end{array}$$

2

$$\begin{array}{r} 8 \\ - 4 \\ \hline \end{array}$$

$$\begin{array}{r} 9 \\ - 3 \\ \hline \end{array}$$

3

How many groups? _____

How many in each group? _____

How many altogether? _____

4

437 has:

[   ] hundreds, [   ] tens

and [   ] ones.

5

Write the missing numbers.

90, 89, 88, _____ ,

86, _____ , 84

6

What part is coloured?

_____ out of _____

7

MEASUREMENT

I pay $2.00 for an ice cream costing $1.00.
How much change will I get?

_____

8

Tick. In 1 minute I can:

jump 10 times ____

eat breakfast ____

9

How many squares make up the shape?

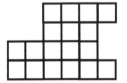

_____

10

How wide is your doorway?

less than a metre ____

more than a metre ____

about the same as a metre ____

11

Which has the greater volume?
Circle it.

12

GEOMETRY

Join all the dots to cover the surface.

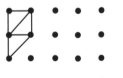

13

Colour the shapes which have curved surfaces.

14

Draw the side view.

My Holiday

During the school holidays I went to stay with my Nan and Pop in Sydney. I went on the plane with my little sister.

Nan and Pop have two dogs. One is a border collie named Ben. The other is half shih tzu and half chihuaha and its name is Chi Chu. We took the dogs down to the lagoon every day and they ran and chased the seagulls but they never caught them.

Pop is a really good cook. He makes stews in the crockpot and he stir-fries vegetables in his wok.

1 The dogs chase (Nan / seagulls / dogs).

2 Pop cooks (ice-cream / stews / stir-fry) in a wok.

3 Nan and Pop live in

_____ .

4 Who is the best cook—Nan or Pop?_____

5 Write three words with *tt* like *little*.

_____ _____ _____

6 Write at least three words that mean *good*, as in *good cook*.

_____

7 Write words that rhyme with *day*.

_____

8 Cross out the incorrect word.

The dogs ran in the (sea / see).

9 Add *es*, *ing* and *ed* to chase. Be careful with spelling.

_____ _____ _____

10 Write four proper nouns from the text.

_____ _____ _____ _____

11 Complete the sentence with verbs.

The dogs _____ and _____ the seagulls.

12 Write the sentence correctly.   the border collie's name is ben

_____

Mathematics

NUMBER

1

$$4 + 1 = \underline{\quad}$$
$$3 + 4 = \underline{\quad}$$
$$7 + 2 = \underline{\quad}$$

2

$$4 - 2 = \underline{\quad}$$
$$7 - 3 = \underline{\quad}$$
$$9 - 0 = \underline{\quad}$$

3

Colour the correct label.

2 × 4   4 × 4   3 × 4

4

Write in sequence from smallest to largest.

0, 17, 132, 96

____ , ____ , _____ , _____

5

Write the missing numbers.

a) 30, ____ , 28, 27

b) 50, 55, ____ , 65

6

Link: $\frac{1}{4}$

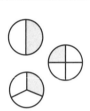 $\frac{1}{2}$

$\frac{1}{3}$

MEASUREMENT

7 Circle the things I can buy with $2.00.

$3.75 $1.95 $1.80

8

Tick. In 1 minute I can:

write my name   ____

write a story   ____

9 Circle the shape with the largest area.

10 List 2 things that are less than 1 metre long.

1. _____

2. _____

GEOMETRY

11 Who has the greater volume?
You ____   Your mother ____
Your father ____
How could you test if you are right?

_____

12

Join the dots to make a tessellating pattern.

• • • • •
• • • • •
• • • • •
• • • • •
• • • • •

13 List 2 things that have this shape.

1. _____

2. _____

14

Help the ant reach its nest.

English

Grandmas

Grandmas love you
good or bad, right or wrong,
morning, noon and night.
Grandmas don't judge
and don't scold.
They love you as you are.
Grandmas bend the rules.
They like to spoil.
They smile and say,
"oh my you've grown"
and "doesn't time fly"
and sooner than later
you'll be taller than Grandma,
but good or bad, right or wrong,
Grandmas love you.

1 Grandmas love you
(morning / all the time / wrong).

2 Grandmas love to
(spoil / boil / toil).

3 Grandmas love you morning,

noon and _____ .

4 What does *time flies* mean?

_____

_____

5 Write three words that start with *wr*.

_____   _____   _____

6 Change one letter to make new words.

bend ___ end   mend   m ___ nd   mind ___ ind

7 Write words that rhyme with *noon*.

s _____   m _____   sp _____

8 Number the words in alphabetical order.

___ morning   ___ noon   ___ night

9 Make the nouns and pronouns plural.

My Grandma loves me. _____

10 Write three nouns from the poem.

_____   _____   _____

11 Complete the sentence with verbs.

Grandmas can _____ .

12 Answer with a sentence.   Do you have a Grandma?

_____

79

1 **NUMBER** **2**

$$5 \atop + \ 2$$ $$3 \atop + \ 1$$ $$2 \atop + \ 4$$ $$9 \atop - \ 4$$ $$8 \atop - \ 3$$ $$5 \atop - \ 2$$

3

Colour the correct label.

5 groups of 5

3 groups of 3   3 groups of 5

4

Start at 5.
Count by 5s and join the dots.

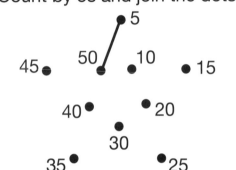

5

Count by 2s and help the frog
jump safely across the lily pond.

6

What part is coloured?

____ out of ____

Colour $\frac{1}{3}$ of the birds.

7

I paid $1.00 for a banana
costing 60c.
How much change did I get?

_____

I paid $2.00 for a pack of crayons
costing $1.50.
How much change did I get?

_____

MEASUREMENT **8**

Show quarter past four.

9

Colour a shape with an area of 10 diamonds.

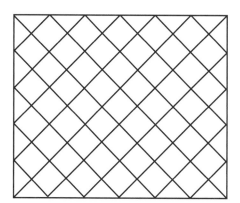

10

List three things which are longer than 1 metre.

1. _____

2. _____

3. _____

11

Tick which has the greatest **volume**.

twig _____

spoon _____

peg _____

biro _____

12

Colour the shapes which show a line of symmetry.

Draw the mirror half.

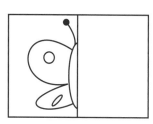

13

How many corners? _____

How many surfaces? _____

How many edges? _____

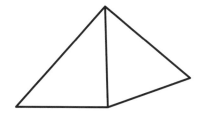

14

Draw the tree from the top view.

Grandpa Remembers

About 70 years ago when I was a small boy my family lived in the bush. My dad was a policeman. He was the only one for about 100 miles (approximately 160 kilometres). As there were no cars in our district the people either rode a horse or travelled in a sulky (which is a cart pulled by a horse) or they walked.

My dad rode a horse to do his job as a policeman and he would be away from home for a week or more at a time travelling around his district. There were no hotels or motels in the bush in those days so he would make camp with his horse beside a dam or a river bank. If he was very lucky a farmer would put him up in the stable with his horse.

For food he would catch fish or snare a rabbit and sometimes the farmers would give him some supplies. One day when Dad was feeding his horse some chaff it accidentally bit his forefinger off. He couldn't find the finger so the horse must have swallowed it. As there were no hospitals or doctors in the bush (we had a bush nurse who used to get around on a horse too) he just wrapped his hand in a piece of his shirt and carried on with his job.

READING & COMPREHENSION

1

The horse swallowed the (bag / finger / rabbit).

2

There were no (horses / cars / policemen) in the olden days.

3 The dad often ate _____ or _____ when he was travelling.

4 Who is telling the story?

5

Find two little words in *hospital*.

_____   _____

6

Find three compound words in the story.

_____   _____   _____

7

Write three words that rhyme with *catch*.

_____   _____   _____

8

Cross out the incorrect words.

He tore a (piece / peace) of shirt. My dad (road / rode) a horse.
(One / Won) day Dad's horse bit his finger off.

9

Write the plurals.

farmer _____   rabbit _____

supply _____   food _____

10

Write three nouns from the story.

_____   _____   _____

11

Complete the sentences with verbs.

Dad _____ his hand in a piece of shirt.

Dad _____ fish for dinner. The horse _____ off
his finger.

12

Write the sentence correctly.

my grandfather's name is eric said robert

_____

© 1999 Tanya Dalgleish and Pascal Press
Reprinted 2000, 2001, 2002, 2003, 2005, 2006, 2007, 2008 (twice), 2010 (twice), 2011

Updated in 2012 for the Australian Curriculum

Reprinted 2014 (twice), 2015, 2016, 2017, 2019 (twice), 2020 (twice), 2021 (twice)

ISBN 978 1 86441 337 3

Pascal Press
PO Box 250
Glebe NSW 2037
(02) 858 4044
www.pascalpress.com.au

Publisher: Vivienne Joannou
Australian Curriculum updates edited by Rosemary Peers
  and answers checked by Peter Little
Typeset by Precision Typesetting (Barbara Nilsson)
  and lj Design (Julianne Billington)
Cover by DiZign Pty Ltd
Printed by Vivar Printing/Green Giant Press